C000128204

;7

The C ... ıt

by Rory N. Mortimore

Edited by
J. T. Greensmith

ISBN 0-900717-83-1

CONTENTS

LIST OF FIGURES

Page

The Chalk of Sussex and Kent

INTRODUCTION

Cretaceous Chalk rims the Weald forming two of the most pronounced geomorphological features of the region, the North and South Downs (Wooldridge & Goldring, 1953) (Figure 1). In the past two decades the furious rate of research on the Chalk in Europe has unravelled many of its mysteries and shown that it is not the 'boring' homogenous and uniform rock that the uninitiated have supposed. As a medium for investigating the interplay between marine transgressions, tectonic events on Europe's western platform and the cosmic origin of rhythmic sedimentation (Milankovitch Cycles) the Chalk has few equals. Nevertheless, the coincidence of key marker flint and marl seams with major bio-events, the origin of many sedimentary structures and the recurrence of particular fossil groups still remain to be explained.

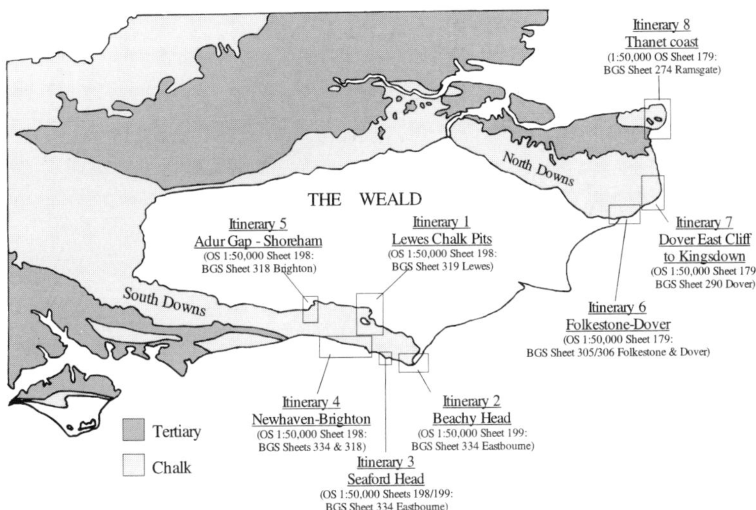

Figure 1. Map of the Chalk of the Weald with Itineraries.

Chalk stratigraphy has been completely revised in the UK and the new terminology for southern England (Table 1) is being used by the British Geological Survey in the course of remapping chalk terrains using satellite imagery and traditional techniques (Bristow, Mortimore & Wood, in prep.). The itineraries described in this guide are an introduction to much of the new work on the Chalk, especially its stratigraphy, sedimentology and tectofacies. The itineraries are designed to illustrate the evidence that suggests that the underlying tectonic structure influenced Chalk sedimentation history. Evidence will also be pointed out to identify transgression-regression events and rhythmic sedimentation.

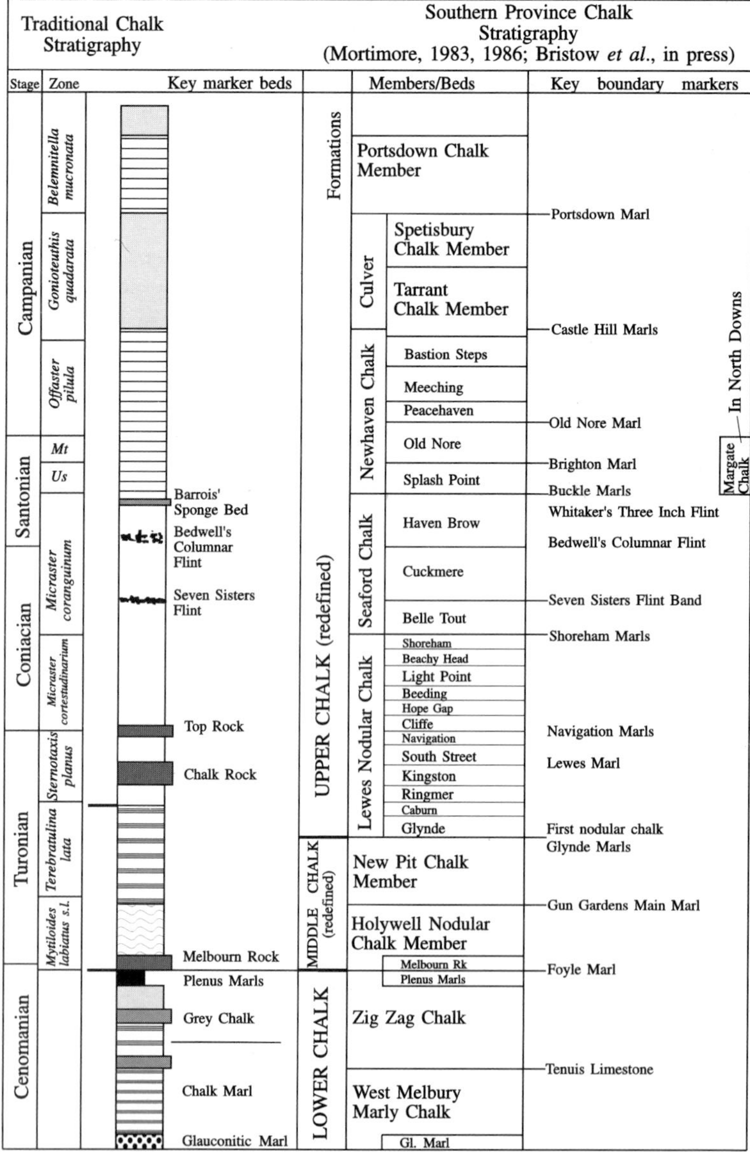

Table 1. Chalk stratigraphic units used in this guide. Formations and Members are those used by BGS for mapping purposes. The traditional zones are shown but the more recent refined zonation is indicated with each itinerary.

The Chalk of Sussex and Kent

The Lewes Pits (Figures 2 & 3), are the starting point because much of the terminology for the lithostratigraphy was developed there and the sections are accessible for detailed study. There are perhaps more Chalk pits in the area around Lewes than anywhere else in the Anglo-Paris Basin, and because the stratigraphy is repeated several times, this allows many key litho- and biostratigraphic marker bands to be identified and their utility for correlation demonstrated. These pits expose the Lower Chalk, Middle Chalk and the Lewes and basal Seaford Chalk (Cenomanian to upper Coniacian).

Between Eastbourne and Brighton, the coastal cliffs provide access to the sediments from the topmost Albian to lower Campanian, complementing and extending the Chalk stratigraphy seen around Lewes. To complete the sections from Eastbourne via Beachy Head to Birling Gap on the Seven Sisters (Albian to upper Coniacian), **a falling tide and 6 hours are required.** Similarly, the Seaford Head section from Hope Gap to Seaford (complete Coniacian, Santonian and Lower Campanian) requires a falling tide and Splash Point near Seaford **must be passed within 2 hours of low tide.** The section can be tackled from the Seaford end more quickly and thus with greater leeway in relation to tides.

Between Newhaven and Brighton, much of the Lower Campanian can be studied on the Newhaven cliffs, Friar's Bay Steps and Bastion Steps, Peacehaven and at Black Rock, without interference from the tide. Access to the upper Santonian beneath the cliffs at Old Nore Point and Friar's Bay, however, requires low tide. This itinerary also includes excellent exposures of Paleocene and Quaternary sediments and sedimentary structures.

The Beeding Quarries in the Adur Valley to the west of Brighton show excellent examples of the contacts between the New Pit, Lewes and Seaford Chalks and illustrate lateral continuity of both the litho- and biostratigraphy. They also illustrate the effects on the Chalk of lateral variations in thickness, and deeper level karstic features.

The North Downs of Kent and Surrey are probably more familiar to geologists than the South Downs. There is less evidence for lateral changes in thickness and lithology in the Chalk of the North Downs partly because the exposures are not as frequent, continuous and accessible as around Lewes. Nevertheless, the River Pit in Dover remains uncorrelated in detail with the nearby coast sections despite the best efforts of many Chalk specialists. There are considerable differences between the Medway and Dover sections and new boreholes through the Medway and Bluebell Hill successions show that even in that relatively short distance the New Pit Chalk varies greatly in thickness and lithology. Other cored boreholes in the Thames Valley illustrate lateral changes from the North Downs to Essex and beneath London. For example, the Lewes Marl which is virtually absent throughout the North Downs returns in the Thames and northwards. Structure contouring on the Plenus Marls and Glynde Marls in the North Downs of Kent and the Thames estuary area shows that, like Sussex, the lateral variations correspond to underlying tectonic structures. All of this information is new and is included in the Guide for the first time.

One of the most useful fossils for marker bed identification and zonation of the White Chalk in the Anglo-Paris Basin is the echinoid *Micraster.* The detailed anatomical and stratigraphical revision of this genus by the late Dr. Philip Drummond (1983), has enhanced the value of *Micraster* and his scheme is included so that GA members and others can test the utility of this method for themselves. In the Newhaven, Margate and Culver Chalks, another echinoid, *Echinocorys,* is the most useful index of horizon. Inoceramid bivalves occur in bands throughout the Chalk and are perhaps the most useful indices for international correlation in the absence of ammonites and belemnites. The key fossil bands are indicated in the Guide, but more details can be found in Mortimore (1986) and Mortimore and Pomerol (1987).

There are still numerous discoveries to be made in the Chalk of the Wealden Region. For example, belemnites in the West Melbury Marly Chalk and Seaford Chalk are rare, as are ammonites in the Middle and Upper Chalk. So, with the help of this Guide, and pointers given in the text, if you find any such, please record the level to within 2 cm and let the author know. By doing so you might be contributing significantly to the stratigraphical knowledge of the Chalk and assisting international correlation programmes.

In addition to macrofossils, levels with an abundance of a particular trace fossil are especially useful for correlation (Mortimore & Pomerol, 1991b). For example, there are two conspicuous *Zoophycos* horizons in the Lewes Chalk. The Cuilfail Zoophycos is found in very soft chalks between the Dover Chalk Rock (Kingston Hardgrounds and Nodular Chalks) and Dover Top Rock (Navigation Hardgrounds) seen on Langdon Stairs, Dover and SW of St. Margaret's at Cliffe, and at the south portal, Cuilfail Tunnel, Lewes. The second conspicuous horizon, the Beachy Head Zoophycos is in the cliffs at the North end of St. Margaret's at Cliffe, Dover and between Birling Gap and Beachy Head on the Sussex coast sections. Horizons of *Zoophycos* chalk have been called 'Bänderkreide' in Germany and 'tiger chalk' in the Crimea, and in both regions form useful marker beds.

Recent oil exploration in southern England has provided excellent seismic sections showing the deep tectonic structure beneath the Chalk. The most important of these seismic lines for interpreting Chalk structures runs north-south down the west side of the Ouse Valley from Lewes to Newhaven. Because the details of the chalk are so well known here, it can be shown that all the major changes in lithology and thickness reflect the position of underlying tectonic lines (Mortimore & Pomerol, 1991a; Mortimore, Pomerol & Lamont-Black, 1996).

A structure contour map drawn on the Bridgewick Marl 1, making use of the numerous borehole geophysical logs as well as quarries, illustrates the complexity of surface tectonic structures in the Downs (Mortimore, 1986b). Isopachyte and lithofacies data, when compared with the structure contours, points to key 'hinge-lines' over which rapid thickness changes and unusual lithologies (e.g. phosphatic chalks, major hardgrounds, channel-scours), are located.

When these data are compared with the seismic sections the key 'hinge-lines' are seen to be underlain at depth by major faults; 'major' structures, such as the Kingston Anticline, are 'mini-inversions' mimicking the much bigger Wealden Anticline.

For the above reasons, the Grey Pit Channel, Strahan's Hardground and phosphatic chalks on the steeper northern limb of the Kingston Anticline are not fortuitously positioned there, but reflect underlying major tectonic lines. The Glyndebourne Hardgrounds lie along the locus of the next major fault to the north and Asham Pits are on the southern boundary of a block (Iford Dome) bounded to the north by the Kingston Anticline hinge-line and to the south by the Beddingham Anticline hinge-line. The thick trough in the centre of the Downs (Mortimore, 1986b; Lake *et al.*, 1987, fig. 23, p. 67), is bounded at depth by faults forming a graben.

The seismic sections, therefore, support the interpretation of tectonic control for the sedimentary hinge-lines seen in the Chalk. This analysis of sedimentation history, using Lewes as a control area, has been extended to the remainder of the Anglo-Paris Basin (Mortimore & Pomerol, 1987; 1991a; Mortimore, Pomerol & Lamont-Black, 1996). Work on the Channel Tunnel has also demonstrated the influence of deep-seated faults on the Gault and Lower Chalk sedimentation (Harris & Warren, 1996).

In addition to structural controls on sedimentation, the Chalk is characterised by rhythmic sedimentation, especially well seen in the West Melbury Marly Chalk (Figures 7 & 23). As a result of the work of Felder (1981) on Campanian and Maastrichtian white or bioclastic chalk rhythms, and Ditchfield and Marshall (1989) and Gale (1989) on the marly chalks, the marl-limestone alternations are shown to contain climatic signals which in turn have been interpreted as cosmically controlled Milankovitch cycles. Felder (1981) found that there was a systematic variation of macrofossil concentrations with the cycles, while Ditchfield and Marshall obtained the first evidence of temperature variations using the $\delta^{18}O$ palaeothermometer. Gale (1989) used these data to suggest a timescale to the rhythms and has also used them for long distance correlation. The $\delta^{18}O$ curve for bulk chalk samples of east Kent (Jenkyns *et al.*, 1994) shows a general cooling during the Late Cretaceous, following a maximum (Table 2) at the Plenus Marls – Melbourn Rock interval (the C/T boundary). Such spikes can be correlated widely across Europe (but with caution because of diagenetic effects) and assist the link between chalk lithologies and marginal sandstones and clays.

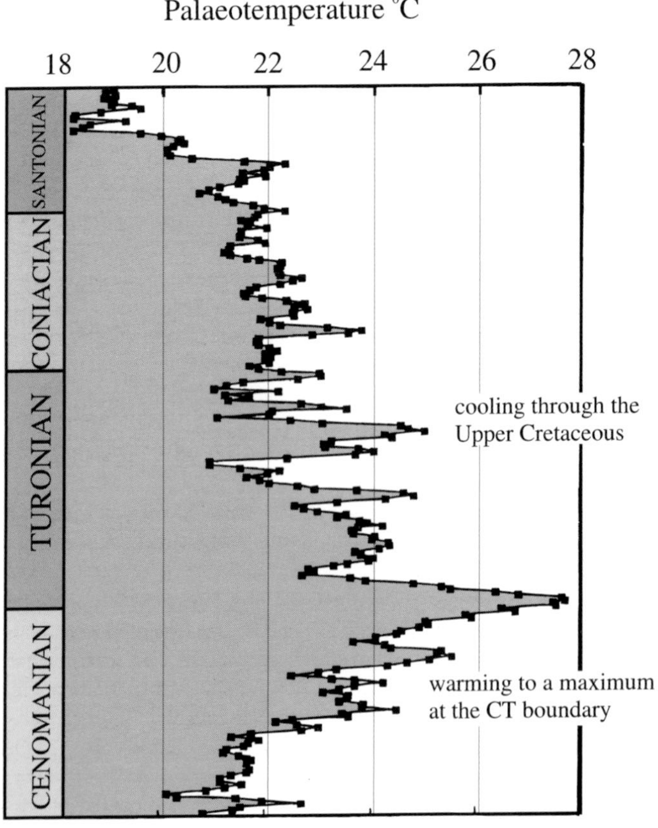

Table 2. Oxygen Isotope Temperature Curve for the Late Cretaceous Chalks East Kent (from Jenkyns et al 1994, fig. 12, p.20)

Geochemical signals, including manganese often in combination with $\delta^{13}C$, are used to identify sea-level fluctuations (Pomerol, 1976, 1983; Pratt *et al.*, 1991) in conjunction with microfossils (e.g. planktonic/benthonic foraminifer ratios). Such geochemical signals are used to support a sequence stratigraphy in relatively deepwater chalks. In marginal areas where the Upper Cretaceous seas lapped onto the land, for example in the Dresden area and Bohemia (Voigt *et al.*, 1994), sea-level fluctuations are expressed as transgressive onlap or regressive offlap in sandy and other clastic rocks, but similar isotope curves to the chalk have been obtained (Ulicný *et al.*, 1993, 1996). The resulting stratigraphy comprising packages of sediment bounded by erosional or transgressive surfaces is the sequence stratigraphy of modern geology. The tectonic setting of particularly the South Downs provides a wonderful example of the impact of sea-level changes on a sea-bed topography regularly modified by tectonic pulses. Hence the specific location of the Southerham Grey Pit Channel which cuts down from the sub-JB Bed 7 sequence boundary and lies above a major basement fault. The dramatic expansion in thickness of the Plenus Marls Beds 1 and 2 at Beachy Head corresponds with a very widespread sub-Plenus Marls erosion surface and a sub-Bed 3 erosion surface followed by an equally dramatic widespread pulse of transgression bringing with it the belemnite *Actinocamax plenus*. The localities where extreme thinning or thickening occur are closely associated with known tectonic structures. The Glyndebourne Hardground 1 and Strahan's Hardground represent further sequence boundaries in the Middle Turonian and the Brighton Marl a further sequence boundary in the Upper Santonian. In contrast, the Lewes Tubular Flints, which represent an extraordinary deep (up to 3 m) network of silicified burrows (with scratch marks or *Spongeliomorpha*), probably relate to a sea-level high stand. Abundant *Zoophycos* (Bänderkreide) seem to be associated with major lithofacies changes at transgressions (e.g. Cuilfail, Beachy Head and Précy Zoophycos).

Table 3 relates the local Chalk geology of the South Downs to the sea-level curve and sequence stratigraphy of Haq *et al.*, 1987. However, the litho- and biostratigraphical framework for the northwest European chalk and its marginal facies is much more precise than the dating on the Haq curve and the marker beds indicated are those which seem to match the various sequence boundaries most closely based on lateral correlation to marginal facies. For example, the Brighton Marl is within the *Marsupites* Zone at about the same stratigraphic level where Voigt (1929) recognised a transgressive pulse of upper *Marsupites* sediments on upturned *Marsupites* sediments in the Harz Foreland of Germany (E. Voigt, 1929, 1963). Similarly, the maximum transgressive surface in the equivalent of the Plenus Marls in the marginal sandy and conglomeratic sediments of the area around Dresden (Saxony) is the Jefferies Bed 3/4 boundary (the belemnite abundance level) (Voigt *et al.*, 1994).

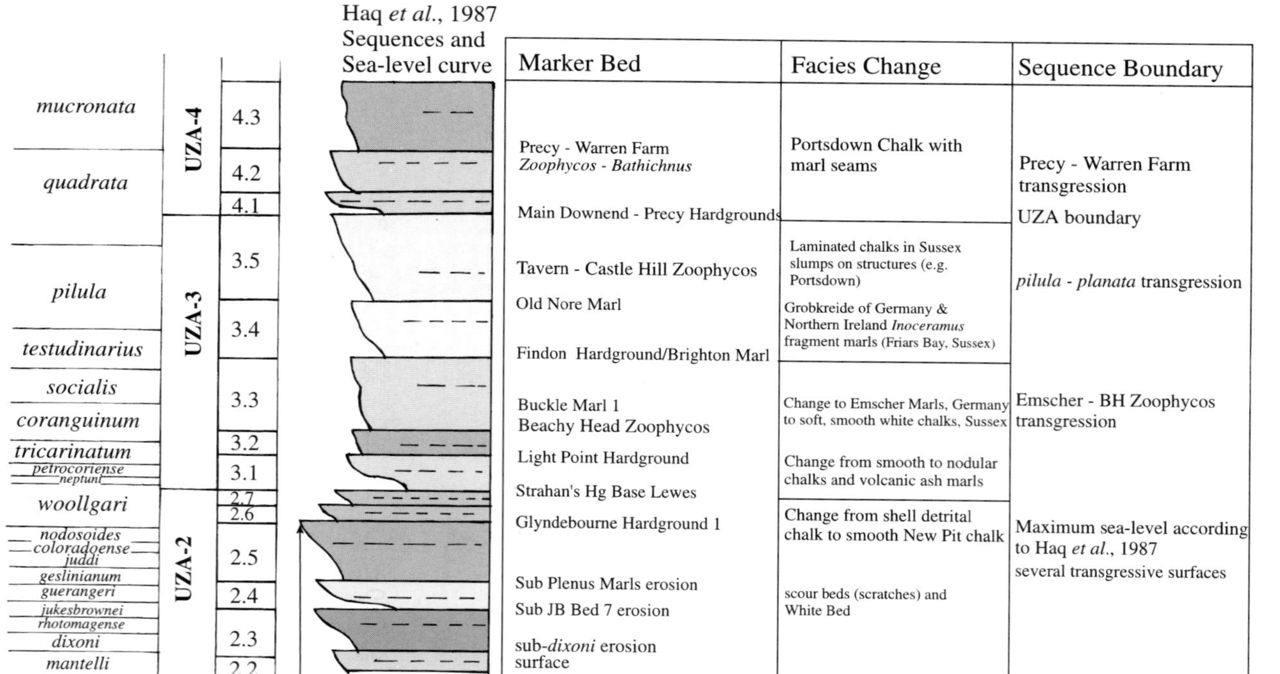

Marker Bed	Facies Change	Sequence Boundary
Precy - Warren Farm *Zoophycos - Bathichnus*	Portsdown Chalk with marl seams	Precy - Warren Farm transgression
Main Downend - Precy Hardgrounds		UZA boundary
Tavern - Castle Hill Zoophycos	Laminated chalks in Sussex slumps on structures (e.g. Portsdown)	*pilula - planata* transgression
Old Nore Marl	Grobkreide of Germany & Northern Ireland *Inoceramus* fragment marls (Friars Bay, Sussex)	
Findon Hardground/Brighton Marl		
Buckle Marl 1 Beachy Head Zoophycos	Change to Emscher Marls, Germany to soft, smooth white chalks, Sussex	Emscher - BH Zoophycos transgression
Light Point Hardground	Change from smooth to nodular chalks and volcanic ash marls	
Strahan's Hg Base Lewes		
Glyndebourne Hardground 1	Change from shell detrital chalk to smooth New Pit chalk	Maximum sea-level according to Haq *et al.*, 1987 several transgressive surfaces
Sub Plenus Marls erosion		
Sub JB Bed 7 erosion	scour beds (scratches) and White Bed	
sub-*dixoni* erosion surface		

Table 3. Possible link between Chalk in marker beds in the Anglo-Paris Basin and the sequence boundaries of Haq et al., 1987.

Even though the chalk contains very little magnetically susceptible material, geologists at Paris University have managed to measure the magnetic reversal from 34 Normal to 33 Reverse just below the Old Nore Marl at Précy, France, the Isle of Wight and Seaford Head (Barchi, 1995, Barchi *et al.*, 1996). Others have found this magnetic reversal to occur in the *Uintacrinus* Zone and it remains to be seen who is correct.

Wray (1990, 1995) has shown that many of the key marker marl seams originated as volcanic ash-fall tuffs (e.g. Glynde 1, Southerham 1, Caburn, Bridgewick 1 and Lewes in the Late Turonian Lower Lewes Chalk). Other widespread marker Marls such as the Shoreham, Brighton and Old Nore Marls

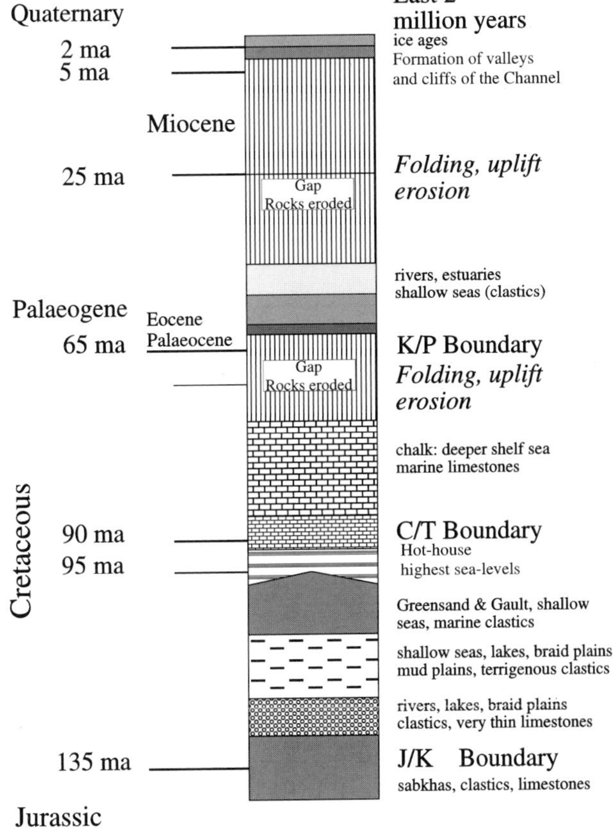

Table 4. Simplified summary of key events and major boundaries for Cretacous, Tertiary and Quaternary of the Wealden Region.

in the Newhaven Chalk may also be tuffs, but these remain to be investigated. The various Chalk lithologies and associated macro, micro-, nanno- and trace fossils of the Wealden region have, therefore, formed in response to tectonic, eustatic, climatic and tephrogenic pulses. Because of these many studies and the complete nature and accessibility of the exposures, it has been proposed by the International Subcommission on Cretaceous Stratigraphy that three of the South Downs sections should become international reference sections. Southerham Grey Pit for the Lower - Middle Cenomanian boundary, Seaford Head for the Coniacian - Santonian boundary and Splash Point at Seaford Head for the Santonian - Campanian boundary. In addition, the Beachy Head exposures of the Cenomanian - Turonian (C/T) boundary compares very favourably in completeness and accessibility with the standard section at Pueblo, USA.

Following the end Cretaceous folding, uplift and erosion of the Chalk, early Tertiary deposits were formed on an uneven and, in places (e.g. Alum Bay, Isle of Wight), a karstic chalk surface. Rivers and estuarine sediments interdigitate with shallow marine clastics in the Wealden region, a further witness to sea-level and climatic changes, and continuing tectonic activity. Remnants of a formerly more extensive cover of Tertiary sediments are exposed at Newhaven and Pegwell Bay. Sea-level, climate and tectonic activity continued to fluctuate with another major phase of folding and uplift in the Miocene (Table 4) which is considered to have formed the Wealden Anticline and the parasitic smaller anticlines such as the Kingston Anticline at Lewes. The Wealden region contains scanty evidence for these later events, but there may be undiscovered pockets of sediment preserved in chalk-dissolution pipes and caves or in the various ages of chalk cements in the cave systems. The Quaternary climatic changes resulting in further sea-level changes and river or 'periglacial' erosion, as ice advanced and retreated, were the final architects of the Wealden landscape cutting into the tectonically uplifted, and tilted terrain. Rivers forming the Greater Seine System (Jones, 1981) originally cut the English Channel and form palaeovalleys in the sea-bed. Final flooding by the sea of the Channel occurred as sea-levels rose after the last ice-age producing new cliff-lines which truncate dry valley systems filled with a variety of late Quaternary cold climate sediments. A study of the Chalk of the Weald cannot ignore these later geological episodes which produced the North and South Downs and the 'White Cliffs' of the present coastline. The itineraries are designed to introduce each of these aspects which saw the region go from extreme hot-house at the C/T boundary some 92 ma to extreme cold-house several times during the ice ages of the last two million years (Table 4).

(For detailed information on the geological history of the pre-Chalk rocks of the Wealden area the companion G.A. Guide No. 55 *Early Cretaceous Environments of the Weald* (Ruffell, Ross & Taylor, 1996) is highly recommended).

SUSSEX CHALK ITINERARIES

Five itineraries are described for the South Downs Chalk. Each itinerary can take a day or selected parts of each can be put together.

Itinerary 1. The Lewes and Mount Caburn Chalk Pits

There are several wonderful alternative routes or walks to the Mount Caburn-Lewes Chalk pits. A day is needed for each to do justice to the geology (Figures 2 & 3). A train takes 1 hour from London Victoria Station to Lewes and the Lewes Pits are in walking distance. A suggested walk is from the station to Southerham and then over Mt. Caburn to Glyndebourne and Glynde (Route 1). Alternatively, a car can be parked for the day in Cliffe Industrial Estate (Figures 3 & 4) and then the same itineraries followed. It is worth starting in the Southerham quarries to get an overview of the Lower, Middle and Upper Chalk.

Traverse 1 takes in the Lower Chalk of Southerham Grey Pit and Machine Bottom, the Middle Chalk of Cliffe Industrial Estate and the Upper Chalk at the north end of Cliffe Industrial Estate and the South Portal of the Lewes Tunnel. All the chalk quarry faces are subject to spalling of flint and chalk and safety precautions are necessary.

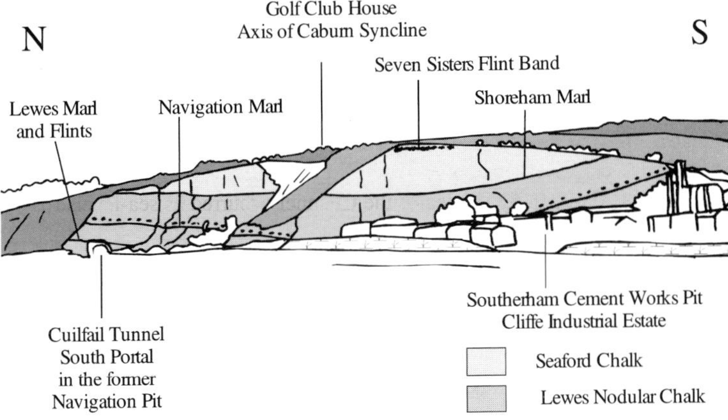

Figure 2. Lewes Mount Caburn Chalk Pits: sketch looking east from the A27 Lewes Bypass, of the Lewes quarries south of Cuifail Tunnel. (NB. The cement works has now been dismantled and replaced by Cliffe Industrial Estate).

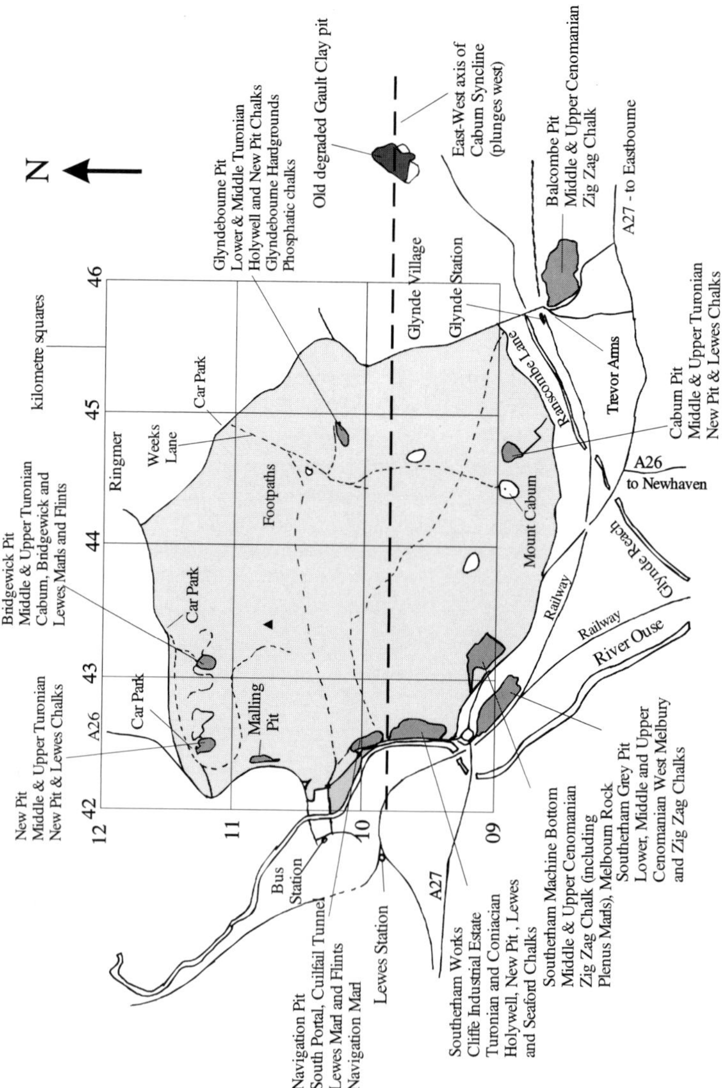

Figure 3. Map of the Mount Caburn area, Lewes, showing main chalk pits and routes to localities.

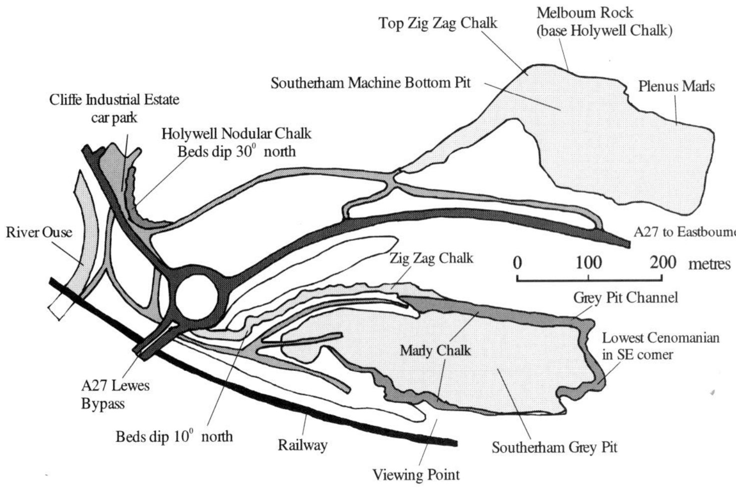

Figure 4. Cenomanian Lower Chalk in Southerham Pits, Lewes.

Locality 1. Southerham Grey Pit (TQ 426090): Firle Estates, Agents Strutt & Parker, Lewes

Summary of geological interest

Lower Chalk (West Melbury Marly Chalk & Zig Zag Chalk: Lower Chalk lithostratigraphy: Lower and Middle Cenomanian biostratigraphy: Cenomanian sedimentary events.

Excavated close to the crest of the Kingston Anticline, Southerham Grey Pit is one of the most famous and stratigraphically important Lower Chalk localities in Northwest Europe (Figures 3 & 4). It contains an unusually sharp contact between the Chalk Marl and Grey Chalk, an erosional channel around the mid-Cenomanian and abundant fossils which have been collected and studied in recent years. As a result, key lithological and fossil marker units and bands have been identified. Unlike many other pits and sea cliffs, Southerham provides safe and continuous access to most of the Lower and Middle Cenomanian.

(As in any pit, it is prudent to be aware of any dangerous, loose or overhanging blocks).

Before studying the detailed geology, it is worth walking to the viewing point (Figure 4). From here look south over the railway to the plain of the River Ouse. Two bumps known as 'The Rises' comprise Lower Chalk resting on Gault. There is no Upper Greensand in the area. The great gap in the Chalk hills, which nearly

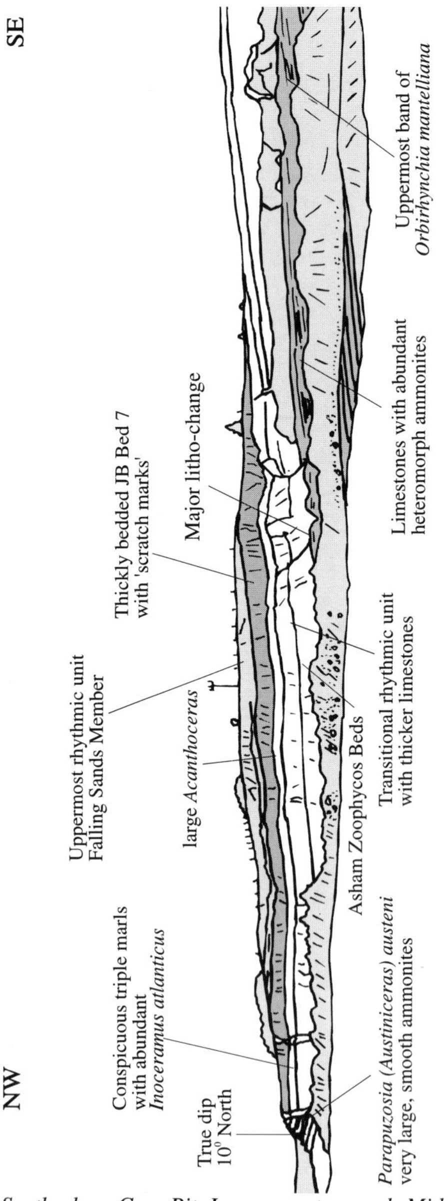

Figure 5. Southerham Grey Pit, Lewes, western end: Middle and Upper Cenomanian Zig Zag Chalk with Asham Zoophycos Beds and JB Bed 7 (JB7).

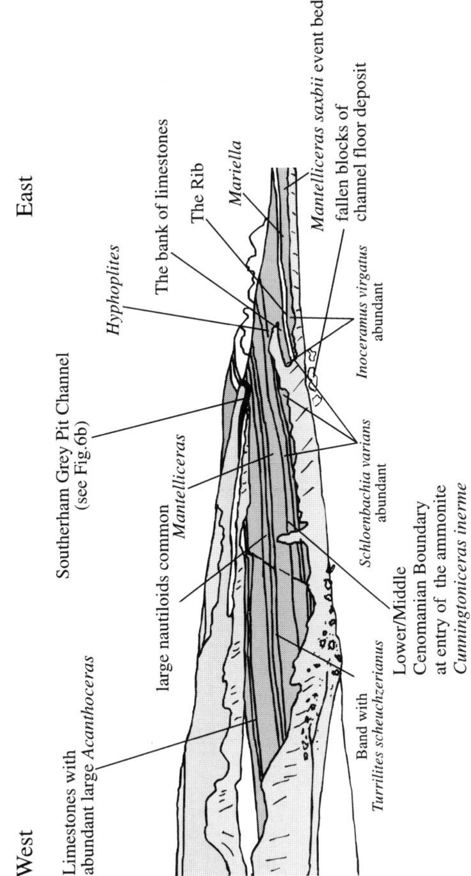

Figure 6a. Southerham Grey Pit, Lewes, eastern end: Lower and Middle Cenomanian West Melbury Marly Chalk.

surround the Ouse at this point, has formed across the Kingston-Beddingham Anticlines. In contrast, the high ground of Mount Caburn to the North has formed in Upper (Lewes) Chalk in the Caburn Syncline, a good example of inverted topography.

Looking north from the viewing point towards the entrance of the pit, the layers can be seen dipping north at 10°. Following the face eastwards beneath the electricity pylon, is a relatively massive bed of chalk containing lenticular,

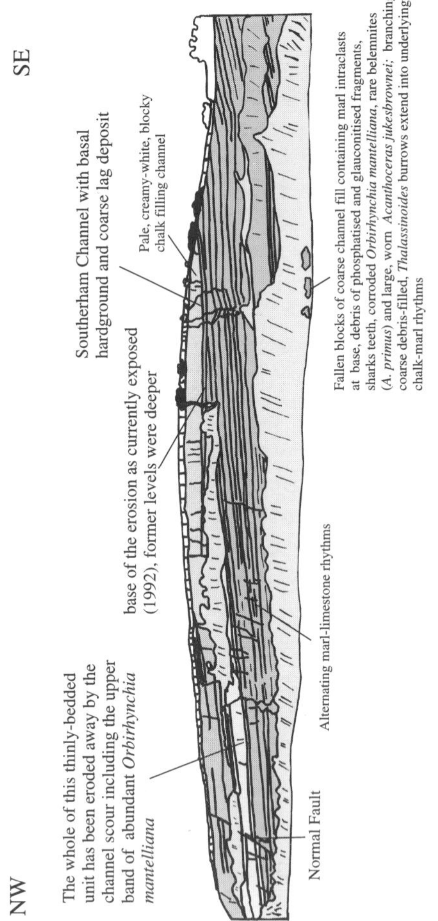

Figure 6b. Southerham Grey Pit Channel.

laminated structures (Figure 5). This is Jukes-Browne Bed 7 of the Dover section (Jukes-Brown & Hill, 1903) and the 'laminations' are considered to be the 'scratched horizon' of Kennedy (1969). Interpretation of these structures, which can be correlated from the eastern Paris Basin to southern England, is still controversial. They have been variously interpreted as trace fossil scratch marks or as non-biogenic sedimentary structures. If, as some think, they are gutter-casts then this unit could represent shallow water within the storm-wave zone. The best place to study these structures is at Falling Sands, Beachy Head (Figures 19 & 20).

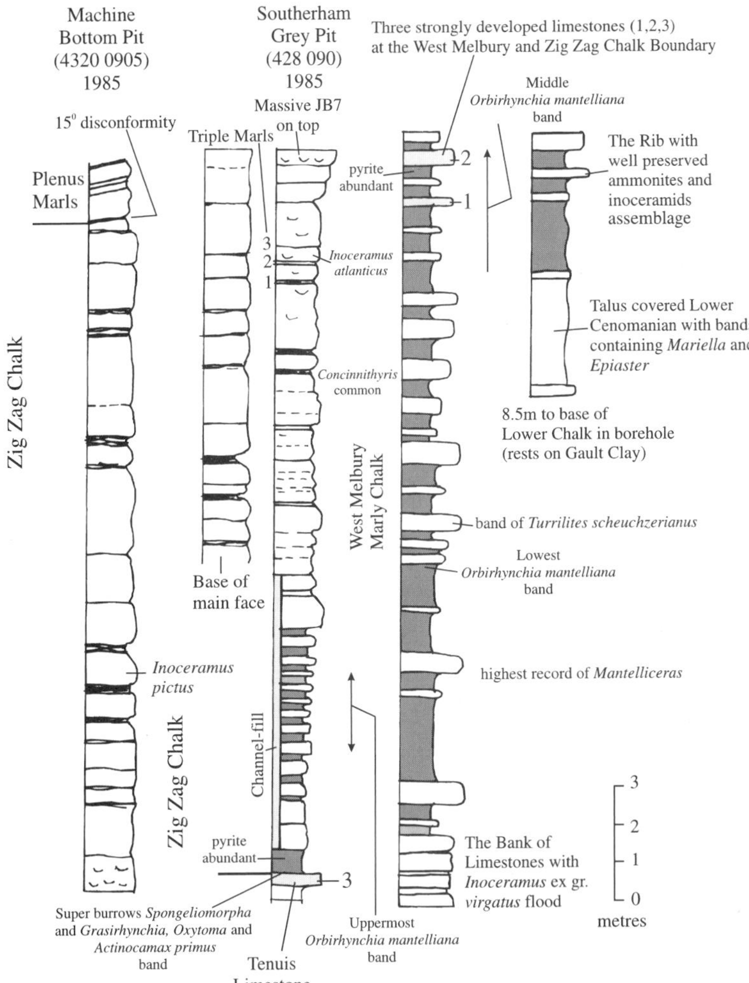

Figure 7. Geological section of Southerham Grey and Machine Bottom Pits.

Beneath the massive JB7 are some 10 m of rhythmic, thickly bedded limestones interbedded with thinner but conspicuous marl seams. This latter unit is known locally as the Transitional Unit and contains abundant and superb examples of *Zoophycos* (Asham Zoophycos Beds, after the Asham Pits on the east side of the Ouse valley). This Transitional Unit rests sharply (the major lithological break) on the underlying marl-limestone rhythms of the typical Chalk Marl (the marls are thicker or equal in thickness to the limestones). The regular falls of debris from these three units provide a rich source of macrofossils and mesofossils, *Inoceramus* ex gr. *pictus* and the ammonite *Calycoceras* fall from beds resting on and above the massive JB7. *Inoceramus atlanticus* occur at the northwestern end of the pit (often in the large fallen blocks), where a conspicuous unit of 'Triple Marl seams' are a guide (Figure 4). Very large ammonites *Parapuzosia (Austiniceras) austeni* are found in beds immediately, and for some metres, below JB7, and 36 large *Acanthoceras jukesbrownei* (Spath) were lifted by excavators from one layer at the base of the massive JB Bed 7 during construction of the adjacent section of the A27. These ammonites are regularly found in rock-falls from this level. Fragments of large acanthoceratids (e.g. *Acanthoceras (Acanthoceras) rhotomagense)* are common in the rock falls from the Transitional Unit.

Lower Cenomanian West Melbury Marly Chalk (Chalk Marl) is present at the far eastern end of the pit where a distinctive 'bank' of limestones is underlain by a thin rib of limestone (200 mm thick). The bivalve *Inoceramus* ex gr. *virgatus* is abundant at this level. In the lowest beds, exposed southwards by the northerly dip, echinoids *Epiaster?* have occasionally been found. Throughout this eastern face ammonites are common particularly *Schloenbachia varians* (J. Sowerby) and less commonly the Lower Cenomanian indices *Mantelliceras saxbii* (Sharpe) and *Mantelliceras mantelli* (J. Sowerby) and *Mariella,* all in specific bands. *Mantelliceras saxbii* occurs in a special band known as an event bed in which *Mantelliceras* dominates over *Schloenbachia.*

Above the 'bank' of limestones each of the succeeding hard nodular limestone layers has yielded well preserved assemblages of *Schloenbachia varians, Mantelliceras mantelli, Hyphoplites, Forbesiceras* and a band of well preserved large nautiloids. A gap between proven Lower and Middle Cenomanian ammonite records was thought in exist in this pit (Lake *et al.*, 1987, fig. 16, p.53), but careful bed by bed collecting in recent years has yielded *Mantelliceras mantelli* from higher levels so that now there is a gap of some 2 m between the last Lower Cenomanian *Mantelliceras* and the first Middle Cenomanian *Cunningtoniceras inerme* and overlying *Acanthoceras.* A conspicuous band of limestone across the middle of the face (Figure 6a) contains well preserved *Turrilites scheuchzerianus* (Bosc) which, like the other fossil marker beds, has been traced through northern Europe as a bio-event.

The uppermost band of *Orbirhynchia mantelliana* (J. de C. Sowerby) is the most easily identified (Figure 7) containing the most abundant examples of this fossil. Several conspicuous limestone layers are present in the upper part of the West Melbury Marly Chalk (Chalk Marl), and contain abundant *Turrilites scheuchzerianus, Turrilites costatus* (Lamarck), *Acanthoceras* and, towards the uppermost '*Orbirhynchia mantelliana* band', numerous scaphitids and *Sciponoceras* (Figure 6). Close to the middle *O. mantelliana* band are two prominent limestone bands above which is a silty brown marl containing moulds of many fossils including rare *Actinocamax primus*. This marl corresponds with the 'Cast Bed' of Dover-Folkestone. The immediately underlying limestone contains *Inoceramus tenuis* and this so-called Tenuis Limestone is used by the BGS to map the boundary between the West Melbury and Zig Zag Chalk members (Bristow *et al.*, in prep).

Many of the limestone bands can be correlated over great distances. The 'rib' and 'bank' of limestones are easily identified above the Glauconitic Marl at Head Ledge (Beachy Head, see below), and many of the Middle Cenomanian limestone bands correlate well with the Dover-Folkestone sections. This lithostratigraphic correlation is supported by the fossil marker bands. In addition, the Middle Cenomanian 'heteromorph' ammonite assemblages correlate well with those of the highly condensed basement beds of Dorset (Drummond, 1970). Individual bands of marl and limestone and specific trace fossil horizons can be correlated in the Zig Zag Chalk (Grey Chalk) but there are also marked lithological changes laterally, such as the presence of a creamy-white limestone unit in the west of the county at Steyning and Washington pits. The Zig Zag Chalk (Grey Chalk) used to be considered the most uniform and persistent of units, but it is clear that there are considerable thicknesses and lithological changes laterally in this unit, as in all other parts of the Chalk.

A further notable feature of this quarry is the Grey Pit Channel which scours down from the 'transitional beds' into the middle Cenomanian marly chalk at the far eastern end of the main face (Figure 6). Boulders of gritty nodular chalk with lumps of oxidised iron pyrites, representing the floor of this channel, can be studied in the scree at the base of the cliff. Intraclasts of marl are incorporated in a melange comprising worn and phosphatised intraclasts as well as fossils such as *Orbihynchia mantelliana*. The 'grit' is primarily made up of glauconitised and phosphatised sand-sized intraclasts and fossil debris. Several types of sharks teeth have also been found. The whole melange is extensively bioturbated with the 'grit' piped down along burrows into the underlying marly chalk. Extremely rare belemnites (*Actinocamas primus*) and a large, worn *Acanthoceras jukesbrownei* have also been collected from the coarse channel-fill material, revealing the extent of the downcutting.

The Lewes Lower Chalk pits have long been famous for their fish and lobster remains (e.g. Willett Collection, Booth Museum, Brighton). Lobster remains and opal have frequently been obtained from the fallen blocks of the transitional and Zig Zag Chalk lithologies at Southerham Grey Pit by local collectors (e.g. the

Martin family of Neville, Lewes). A crab carapace was also collected in the *I. atlanticus* beds. Other rare fossils include *Ophiomusium* (brittle star) and objects that look like fir cones, but which have been variously interpreted as coprolites or casts of spiral valves of selachians (i.e. stomach valves). Two of the most common fossils at Southerham are *Plicatula inflata* and *Euthymipecten beaveri.* The prominant double limestone labelled H by Kennedy (1969) contains abundant three-dimensional, well preserved inoceramids and ammonites particularly *Schloenbachia, Forbesiceras* and *Acompsoceras.*

Locality 2. Machine Bottom Pit, Southerham (TQ 430092): Firle Estates.

Summary of geological interest

Lower Chalk (topmost West Melbury Marly Chalk & Zig Zag Chalk): Plenus Marls, Melbourne Rock & Mead Marls: Middle and Upper Cenomanian.

Machine Bottom Pit, on the north side of the A27 Eastbourne Road, continues the succession into the Upper Cenomanian but stratigraphically overlaps with the Grey Pit (Figures 2 & 7). There are poor exposures of the uppermost beds of the West Melbury Marly Chalk (Chalk Marl), through a better exposed complete Zig Zag Chalk and Plenus Marls to the Melbourn Rock in the basal Holywell Nodular Chalk. Marker beds (individual marl seams, limestone bands and trace fossil horizons) in the upper part of the Zig Zag Chalk, Melbourn Rock, and the Meads Marls in the Holywell Chalk can be identified and provide a correlation with Beachy Head and Asham. There is a marked change in dip between the Grey Chalk and the Plenus Marls in this pit (Figures 4 & 7).

The benches cut in the Zig Zag Chalk close to the floor of the quarry have provided three-dimensional examples of *Zoophycos* showing both the central and marginal tubes, which are commonly lightly iron-stained.

Locality 3. Cliffe Industrial Estate: Southerham Works Quarry
owned by Crown Concrete Estates, Rugby. (TQ 425095)

Summary of geological interest

Holywell Nodular Chalk, New Pit Chalk, Lewes Chalk, Strahan's Hardground and phosphatic chalk: Lower, Middle and Upper Turonian

Mantell's "*The Fossils of the South Downs*" (1822, Tab.VII) illustrates the extent of the Chalk then exposed at Southerham near the Old Lime Kilns. Parts of this old section still remained when Strahan (1896) and Dibley (1906) described the Lewes Phosphatic Chalk but, until recently, it was degraded and overgrown.

Since 1980 the construction of the Cliffe Industrial Estate has resulted in a complete re-excavation of the whole succession from close to the top of the Melbourn Rock to the Beeding Beds in the Lewes Chalk, providing an outstanding section through the phosphatic chalk (Figures 8 & 9).

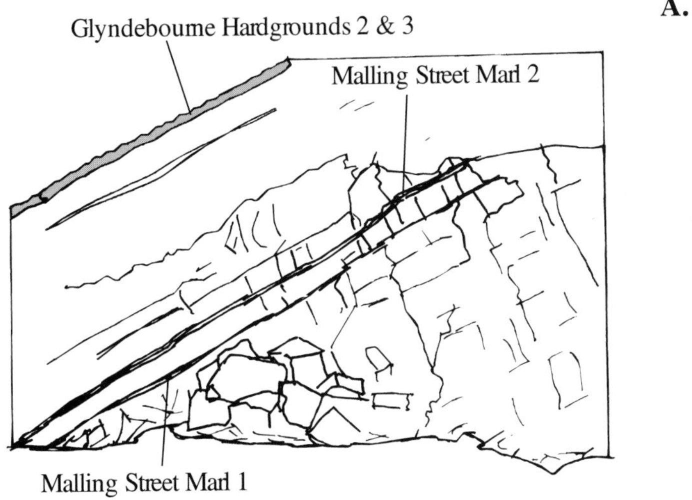

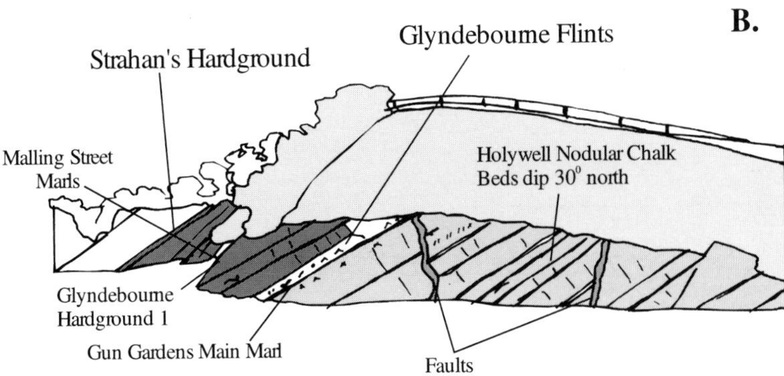

Figure 8. Southerham Works Quarry. Sketches showing the position of key marker beds. A. general view sketched before buildings were constructed. Strahan's Hardground is now behind the industrial unit. B. Position of Malling Street Marls in the corner of the new cut. C. Section north of Strahan's Hardground (next page).

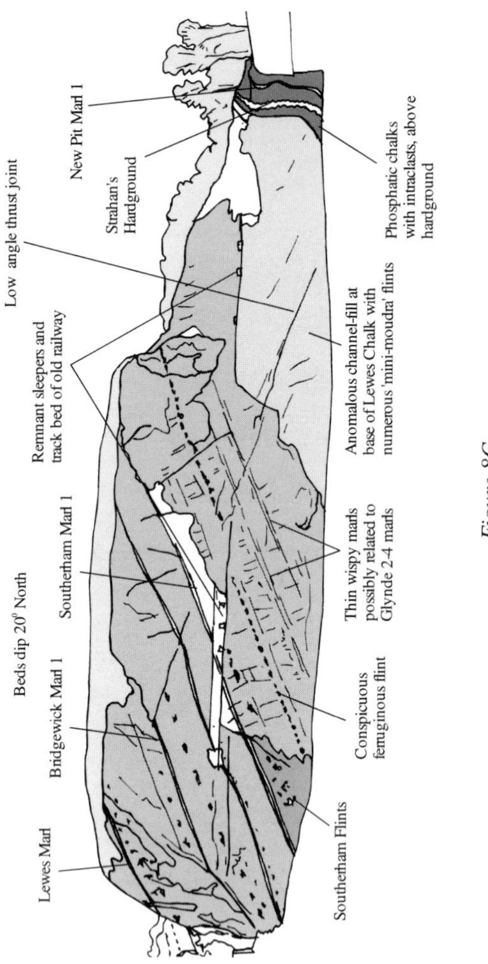

Figure 8C

Section 1. Lower-Middle Turonian Holywell Nodular Chalk

At the southern end of the quarry the beds dip relatively steeply north at between 25° to 30°. The lowest marker horizons that can be identified are the Holywell Marls and the griotte chalks with bands of abundant *Mytiloides.* Towards the northern end of this first section the Gun Gardens Marls and the Glyndebourne Flint are present. Detailed correlation with Glyndbourne Pit and Beachy Head is thus possible.

The section is most easily studied by first identifying the steeply dipping Gun Gardens Main Marl (Figure 8A). It is found towards the stratigraphically highest part of the section (north) and is associated with abundant nodules of red-weathering iron pyrites. The small flints above the marl are not always easy to identify, but excavation of the chalk immediately above the marl usually yields several of them. Two normal faults filled with a weathered gouge complicate the section.

Early *Mytiloides* have been obtained from the lowest beds followed by the succession of *Mytiloides* taxa recognised at Glyndebourne. The brachiopod-*Conulus* assemblage above the Gun Gardens Main Marl, seen at Glyndebourne and Beachy Head, is also repeated here.

Section 2. Malling Street Marls and Glyndebourne 2-3 equivalents.

The section up to the Malling Street Marls is poor, but the Marls are well exposed at the south corner behind the first building (Figure 8A). Red, iron-stained nodular beds, the lateral equivalent to Glyndebourne Hardgrounds 2 and 3, are present in the succeeding face behind the first building. Bands of *Conulus subrotundus* assist the correlation.

Section 3. Strahan's Hardground to Lewes Marl.

Scree covers the section up to Strahan's Hardground, but from there to the Cliffe Hardground the stratigraphy is well exposed. The general stratigraphical position of the Lewes Phosphatic Chalk is most easily fixed by working down from the Southerham Marls and Flints. This leads through an anomalously thick and flinty sequence in which the Glynde Marl is difficult to identify, but the griotte marls above Strahan's Hardground probably correlate with New Pit Marl 3. Beneath Strahan's Hardground is another well developed nodular chalk seam and on its surface is the thick, plastic New Pit Marl 1.
In the succeeding section, the position of the Southerham, Caburn, Bridgewick and Lewes Marls and flints can be seen. Two of the flint bands in the Glynde Beds are particularly conspicuous, emphasising the difference with the North Downs where flints are less obvious at this level. In addition to the marker marl seams and flints that are of great importance to correlation in the Chalk, the discovery, for the first time in Sussex of (i) *Micraster michelini* (Agassiz) immediately below the Caburn Marl in Caburn Pit, a level comparable with the same marl seam at Langdon Stairs, Dover, where Stokes (1975) has recorded

similar forms and (ii) *Bicavea rotaformis* (Gregory), also in Caburn Pit in the nodular beds immediately above the Caburn Marl, a level comparable with Dorset and the Isle of Wight where Rowe had collected this rotiform bryozoan (Rowe, 1908), has greatly facilitated correlations along the south coast.

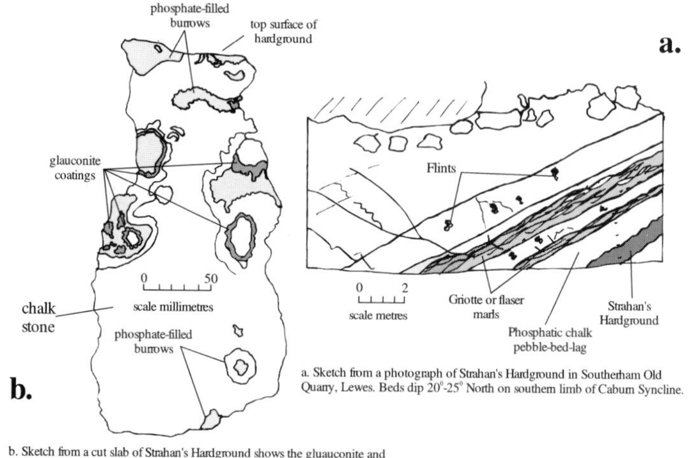

a. Sketch from a photograph of Strahan's Hardground in Southerham Old Quarry, Lewes. Beds dip 20°-25° North on southern limb of Caburn Syncline.

b. Sketch from a cut slab of Strahan's Hardground shows the gluauconite and phosphate coated top surface and burrow walls of the hardground. Late stage burrows are filled with a phosphatic chalk lag and bored pebbles of hard chalk.

Figure 9. Details of Strahan's Hardground.

Walking north through the old quarry, the re-emergence of the Lewes Marl and Flints and the Navigation Marls on the south flank of the Caburn Syncline illustrates the changing dip of the beds from a 30° dip of the north at the southern end of the quarry to a 5° dip south by the south portal of the Cuilfail Tunnel. At the far northerly end of the old quarry (TQ 425098) the Cliffe Hardground is easily studied on the upper bench of the road cutting. The Shoreham Marls and the Belle Tout Marls form grooves in the high part of the cliff and the conspicuous Seven Sisters Flint can be seen at the very summit of the quarry face (Figures 2 & 12).

Locality 4. South Portal of the Cuilfail Tunnel in the Navigation Pit and Chandlers Yard (TQ 425100)

Summary of geological interest

Top Kingston Beds, Lewes Marl and Flints, Lewes nodular chalks, Cuilfail Zoophycus, Navigation and Cliffe Beds: Turonian – Coniacian Boundary problems.

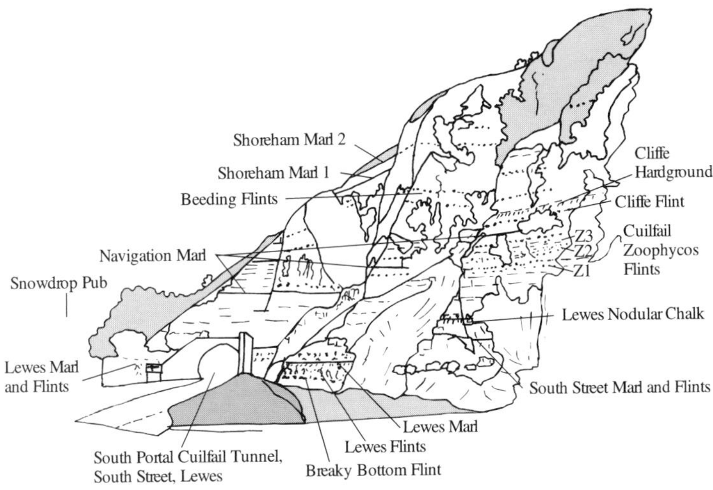

Figure 10. The former Navigation Pit and Chandler's Yard at the South Portal, Cuilfail, Lewes Tunnel. Sketches of the old quarry faces showing key marker beds.

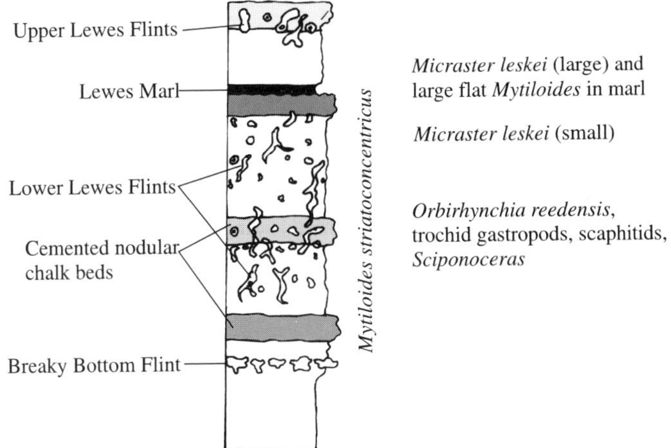

Figure 11. Geological section showing the Lewes Marl and the special forms of tubular flints (Lewes Tubulars) and associated biostratigraphical markers, at the Cuilfail Tunnel South Portal exposure.

Recent construction of the Cuilfail Tunnel (1976-78) has partly obscured the section formerly exposed in the Navigation Pit. As a result of the southerly dip the complete lower Lewes Chalk up to the Lewes Marl was exposed during the construction of the tunnel. (Figures 10 & 11). The stratigraphic studies were complemented by three rotary cored boreholes and the logging of an old well sunk through the hillside. The Lewes Marl is still well exposed in the faulted section immediately south of the tunnel portal on the eastern face, dipping south on the northern limb of the Caburn Syncline. The upper Kingston, South Street, Navigation and Cliffe Beds are progressively accessible in freshly cut faces on the southerly approaches to the tunnel. The same fossil assemblages as indicated at Bridgewick, below and above the Lewes Marl can be collected. In addition the large inflated *Sternotaxis [Holaster] placenta* (Agassiz) and *Echinocorys* are found in the upper South Street Beds and the soft Cuilfail Zoophycos Chalks of the Navigation Beds. The three bands of *Zoophycos* flints are a particular feature.

The interval between the Lewes and Navigation Marls is at its maximum thickness in this section and it is in this interval that the Turonian – Coniacian boundary must occur. Late Turonian *Mytiloides* are found in the South Street Beds and, with the evidence from Shoreham Cement Works, probably range up to the Navigation Hardgrounds. However, *Cremnoceramus* ex gr. *inconstans* group inoceramids have been found in the Navigation beds (these inoceramids are currently being rethought by the specialists and their identification may change) and *Micraster normanniae* enters above the Lewes Nodular Chalks. This has led to the suggestion that the base of the Coniacian may coincide with the base of the Navigation Beds rather than at the top of these beds (Bailey *et al.*, 1983, 1984; Mortimore & Pomerol, 1987; Pomerol *et al.*, 1988).

The remainder of the quarry face up to the Seven Sisters Flint Band beneath the Golf Club House can be examined in two precipitous grassy slopes (Figure 12). Details of this stratigraphy are obtained more easily on the coast and at Shoreham Cement Works. Key marker bands such as the Shoreham Marls form conspicuous grooves in the cliff face so that the overall stratigraphy and thicknesses can be identified.

The University of Brighton's South Street Research Borehole was drilled in the floor of Chandler's Yard Pit to provide a control geophysical log through the Middle Chalk and Lower Lewes Chalk. The non-standard profile that resulted provided unexpected information on the position of the Lewes Phosphatic Chalk and thicknesses of the Chalk.

Incidentally, if you wish to visit the North Portal of the Cuilfail Tunnel, along Malling Street, the exposures include the New Pit Marl 2 and the Glynde Marl 1 (Figure 13) (also see Locality 11).

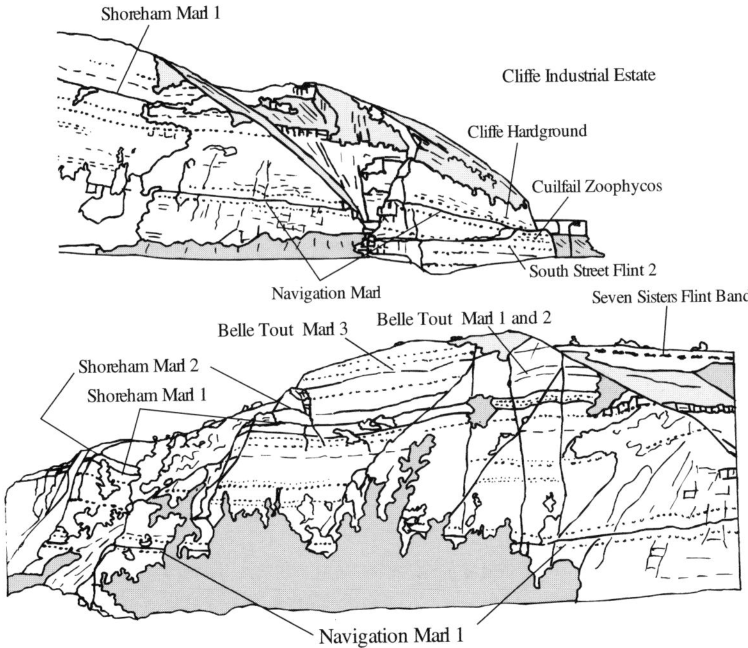

Figure 12. Sketches showing key marker beds in the cliff exposures south of the Cuilfail, Lewes Tunnel.

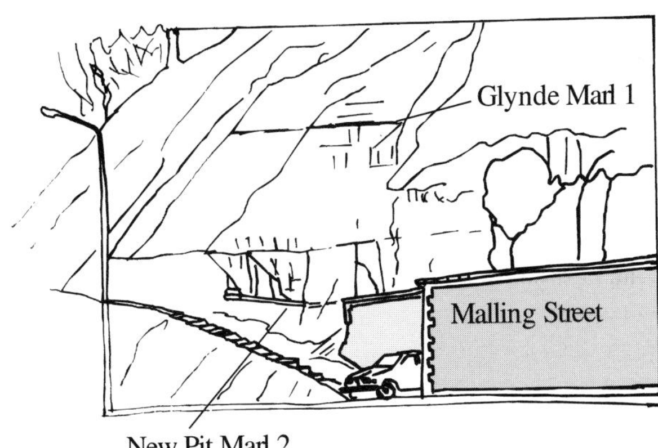

Figure 13. Cliff exposures at the North Portal of the Cuilfail, Lewes Tunnel, along Malling Street, showing the position of the New Pit and Glynde Marls.

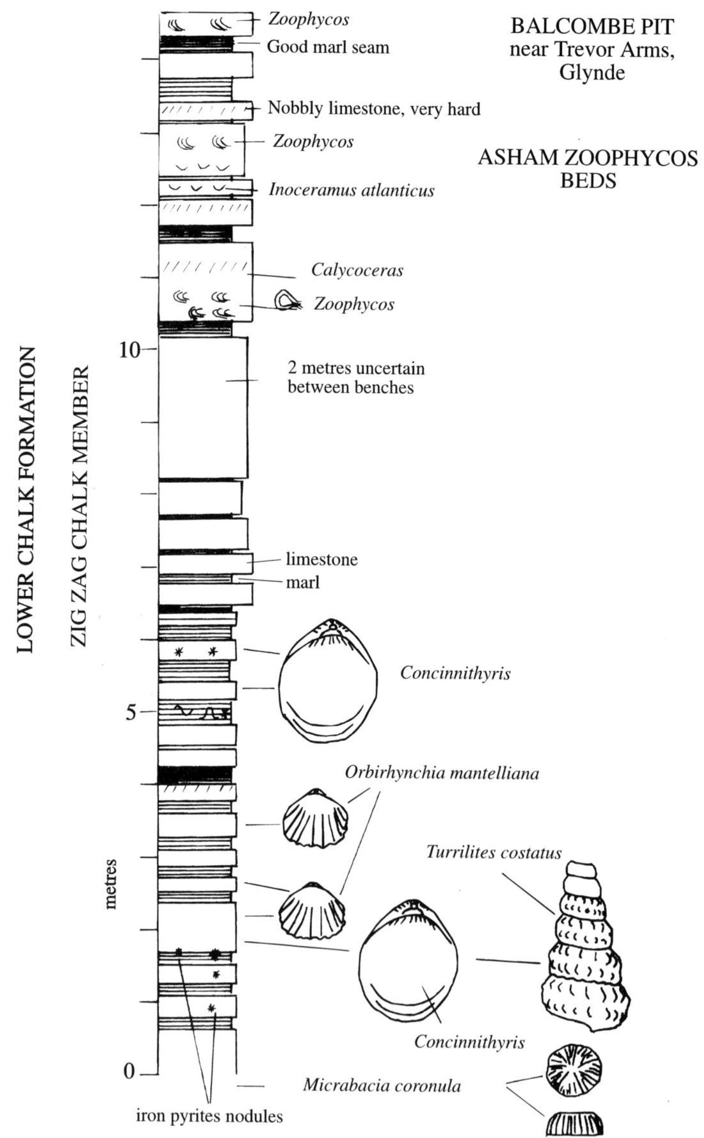

Cast Bed and Tenuis Limestone probably just below current working depth

Figure 14. Lower Chalk exposed in Balcombe Pit, Glynde. Cast Bed and Tenuis Limestone are probably just below the current base of pit.

Locality 5. Balcombe Pit. Glynde (TQ 460085)

Summary of geological interest

Lower Chalk (West Melbury Marly Chalk and Zig Zag Chalk junction on the crest of the Kingston Anticline).

Balcombe (or Newington's) Pit is still worked in benches, which makes obtaining an accurate measured section difficult (Figure 14). Beds below the uppermost *Orbirhynchia mantelliana* band are exposed, yielding the same abundance of Middle Cenomanian ammonites seen in Southerham Grey Pit. Large acanthoceratid ammonites are fairly common in the upper beds. *Calycoceras* and large, almost smooth *Parapusozia (Austiniceras) austini* are also found regularly. The main feature of the pit is the change of dip from the northern to southern ends indicating the crest line of the Kingston Anticline.

Locality 6. Caburn Pit (TQ 447089)

Summary of geological interest

New Pit – Lewes Chalk Junction; New Pit, Glynde, Southerham and Caburn Marls: Middle to Upper Turonian

At least a long afternoon is required to walk or drive around the Mount Caburn Pits.

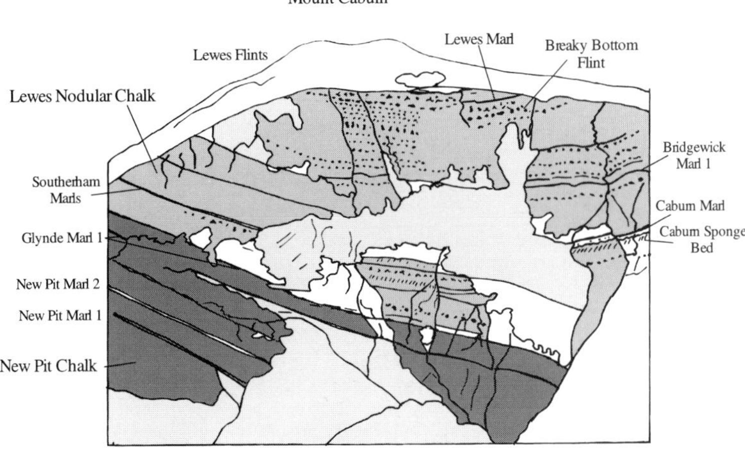

Figure 15. Sketch of the main face of Caburn Pit, looking NW, showing the position of key marker beds. Not all features are shown.

Caburn Pit is approached from the narrow Ranscombe Lane (Figure 3), and is unsuitable for large vehicles, which should be parked in Glynde Village. The Pit has a very high, overgrown and dangerous face and is only suitable for very fit enthusiasts.

Caburn Pit is first referred to in Barrois' major work on the Chalk of England and Ireland (1876), and his "Craie de ranscombe" coincided roughly with the Middle Chalk of the Geological Survey. Caburn Pit is the only major excavation in the Chalk adjoining Ranscombe Lane and must at one time have exposed much of the Zig Zag Chalk, all the Middle Chalk and terminated at the Lewes Marl. Today (1996), the main face of the Pit exposes an excellent contact between the more thickly bedded New Pit Chalk with marl seams and the Lewes Chalk with regular seams of nodular chalk and flint beautifully air-weathered in the higher part of the cliff (Figure 15).

At the base of the main face are the two strongly developed (0.2 m thick) New Pit Marls with their characteristic 'brittle' texture and buff to pale green hue, in contrast to the thinner (0.05-0.1 m thick) Glynde Marl 1 with its black plastic clays. The large, deep water foraminifer *Coskinophragma* is fairly abundant in the weaker marls below and in the Glynde Marls, as well as in the Southerham Marl 1 above. Beds rich in *Inoceramus cuvieri* (J. Sowerby) and *Conulus subrotundus* (Mantell) can be seen between and above the New Pit Marls at the same stratigraphic level as at Beachy Head thus assisting the lithological correlations. The higher part of the face is accessible only via a **hazardous climb which should not be undertaken without expert help and guidance.** These higher beds in the Lewes Chalk contain the Caburn Marl, above which the basal nodular chalks of the Ringmer Beds yield the rotiform bryozoan *Bicavea rotaformis* (Gregory) found here for the first time in Sussex. The surface beneath the Caburn Marl yielded *Micraster (Epiaster) michelini* and an excellent specimen of the Middle Turonian zonal index ammonite *Romaniceras (Romaniceras) deverianum* (d'Orbigny) (figured in Wright & Kennedy, 1981) was obtained from below this Marl in Firle Pit (TQ 464063).

Above the Bridgewick Marls occurs the micrasterid *Roweaster rowei* (Drummond, ms) with a vertical posterior profile which contrasts with the extended 'talon' that this echinoid has in lower beds.

Locality 7. Glyndebourne Pit 1 (TQ 448102).

Summary of geological interest

Holywell Nodular Chalk and New Pit Chalk: Turonian biostratigraphy; tectonics and sedimentation.

The approach to the Glyndebourne pits is along Week Lane (Figure 3) towards Mount Caburn which provides a fine view over the Downs and Glyndebourne Opera House. The break of slope in the lane 200 metres from the road represents the Plenus Marls – Melbourn Rock (base Holywell Nodular Chalk) contact.

Glyndebourne Pit 1 is remarkable for the exposures of phosphatic chalk hardgrounds close to the boundary between the Lower and Middle Turonian. These orange and green stained nodular chalks were first referred to in Osborne White's revision Lewes memoir (1926) but neither their phosphatic content nor their relationship to Strahan's Lewes phosphatic chalks was considered.

The entrance to the pit on the lower track crosses the overgrown contact between the Plenus Marls and the Melbourn Rock. The first exposures (low cliffs, 2-3 m high) must be some 10 m above this contact as the beds are rich in varieties of *Mytiloides* close to, but not at, the entry of this group. This is confirmed by collections from Beachy Head and Southerham Works Pit. *Orbirhynchia cuvieri* (d'Orbigny) is also common in these lowest exposures, associated with well developed griotte marls and nodular chalks. The *Mytiloides*-rich beds can be

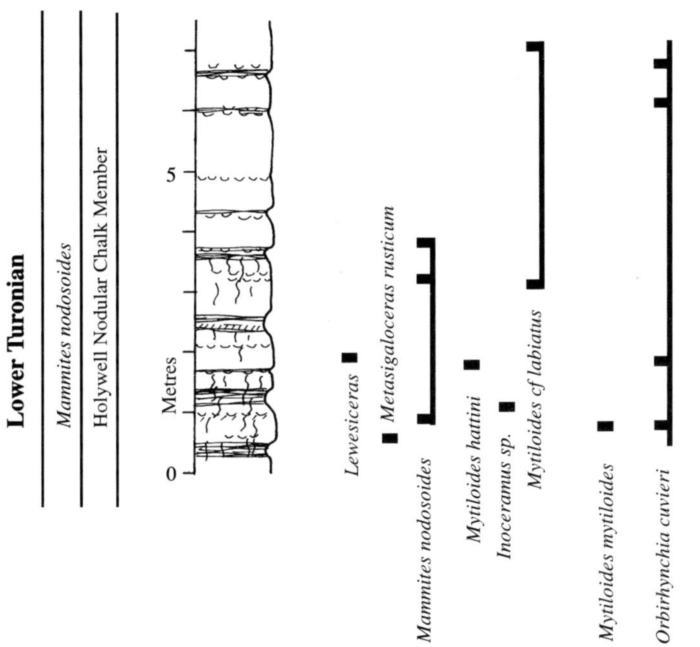

Figure 16. Geological section of the lowest beds exposed in Glyndebourne Pit, near Lewes, showing distribution of ammonites and inoceramids.

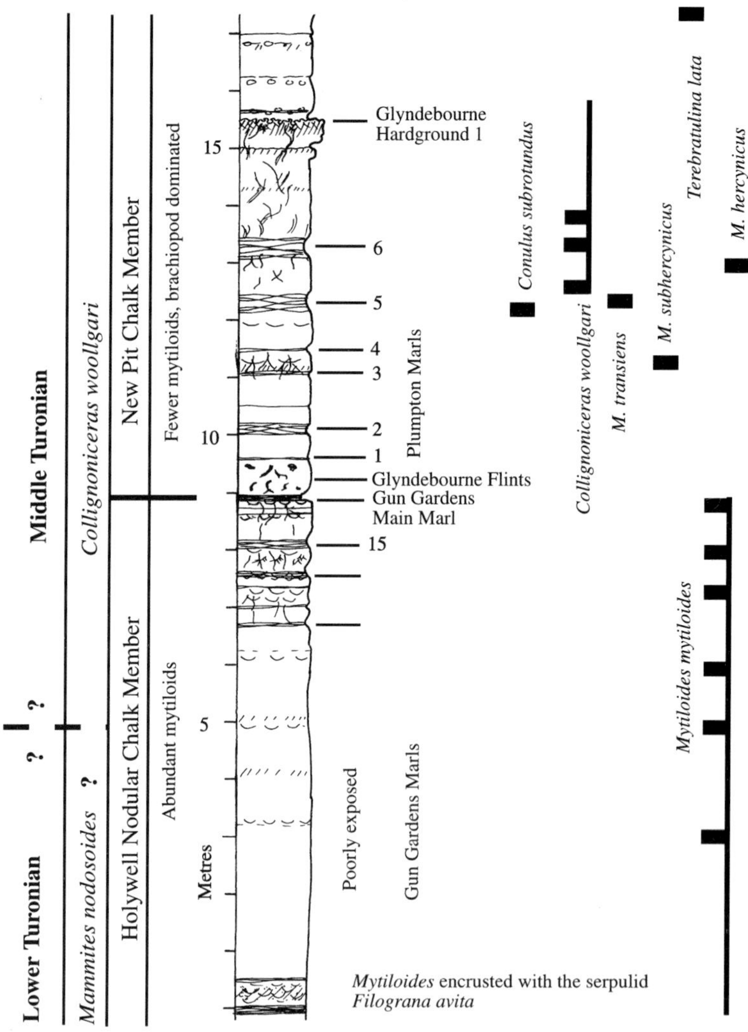

Figure 17. Geological section of the lower part of the main face of Glyndebourne Pit showing the boundary between Holywell Nodular Chalk and New Pit Chalk and the Glyndebourne Flints.

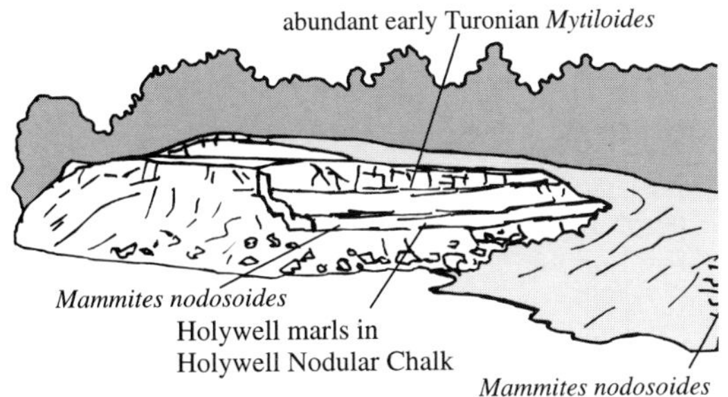

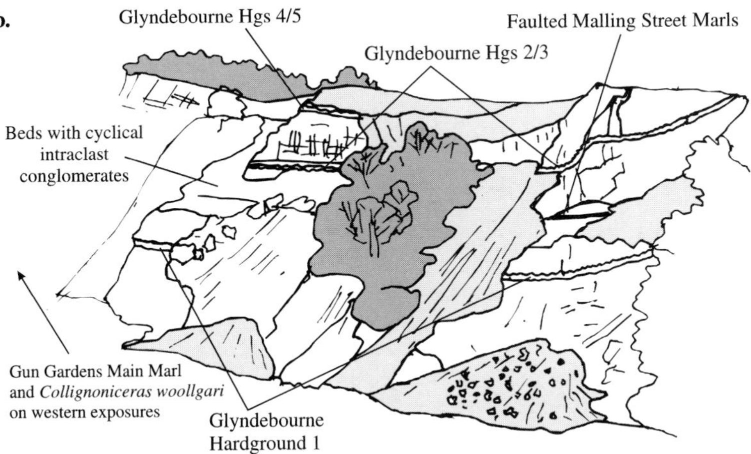

Figure 18. Sketches of Glyndebourne Pit exposures. a. Lowest sections (1988). b. Part of main face showing New Pit Chalk Member with the Glyndebourne Hardgrounds (Hg).

traced through a thickness of 22 m of chalk into the main face of the pit. A range of forms of *Mytiloides* useful for zonal subdivision has been collected here (Figures 16 to 18). The early forms are replaced upwards by *Mytiloides* with alternating bands of *Mytiloides mytiloides* and *Mytiloides labiatus.* Beds with *M. subhercynicus* have been located in the lower section of the main face. Inoceramids of the *I. lamarcki* group occur in beds above the Malling Street Marls in the centre of the main face (Figure 18).

Ammonites are not as abundant as the inoceramids, but several important bands are recognised including early mammitids?, *Mammites nodosoides* (Schlüter), *Lewesiceras*, and *Collignoniceras woollgari* (Mantell). These bands provide a means of linking the inoceramid-ammonite assemblages and fixing the Turonian subdivisions in Europe more precisely. In the lowest beds large ammonites with mammitid-like nodes are immediately overlain by true *Mammites nodosoides* and *Lewesiceras*. Each layer can be precisely located within the lithostratigraphy (Figure 17). In the lower beds of the main face a band of small finger-tubular flints has been identified. This flint band also occurs at Southerham Works Pit, Plumpton Pit, Beachy Head and St. Martin Plage north of Dieppe. It has also been found in the Faircross borehole, Berkshire, and is clearly of great utility for correlation and is thus named the Glyndebourne Flint. This flint seam helps to identify the lowest horizon of *Collignoniceras woollgari* so far definitely found in southern England. This is well below the conventional zonal boundary between the *M. labiatus* and *Terebratulina lata zones* taken here at the lowest Malling Street Marl. The Lower – Middle Turonian boundary is thus fixed in a more compatible position in relation to the inoceramids in the chalk facies of northwest Europe and confirms the speculative position of this boundary suggested by Wright & Wright (1951) and Hancock, Kennedy & Wright (1977, p. 153 & fig. 2). At this same horizon the lithological change to the New Pit Chalk (more massive chalks, entry of flints), is associated with a change in the trace fossils and the replacement of *Mytiloides*-dominated chalks by brachiopod-*Conulus subrotundus* -bearing chalks.

Two types of trace fossil are a feature of the Turonian Holywell Nodular Chalk; one is a sinuous slender tube (2-3 mm diameter) with green glauconite coated walls and the other a larger cylindrical form (10-15 mm diameter), penetrating the sediments vertically and cross-cutting the griotte marl bands. This latter tube has subhorizontal rings, a segmented structure. These two types of trace fossil are particularly common in the Holywell Beds and can be recognised all the way to Shillingstone in Dorset and Troyes in the eastern Paris Basin. The trace fossils also illustrate that many of the griotte marls must have an early synsedimentary origin rather than a post-depositional pressure solution origin.

Several faults complicate the stratigraphy of the main face, but the orange stained hardgrounds can be traced through the faults. The second and third hardgrounds unite when traced laterally, occluding a marl seam. These layers were taken by Osborne White (1926) as the junction between the *M. labiatus* and *Terebratulina lata* zones. Recently *T. lata* (Etheridge) has been found here in and below these hardgrounds down to the Malling Street Marls. The marls are badly faulted, acting as layers of preferential deformation but still showing the presence of black, plastic clays. Late forms of *Mytiloides* have been obtained up to these marls, which are now taken as the zonal boundary marker. A second band of *Collignoniceras woollgari* is now identified just above the marls as several specimens have been collected in this section.

It is possible but dangerous to climb onto the steeply sloping ledges at the top of the face (**this should not be undertaken without expert assistance**). During the 1980 Geologists' Association meeting Chris Wood was rewarded with finding a well preserved *Scaphites* from the second hardground. A second echinoid band with fairly common *Conulus subrotundus* is also present.

There is no simple correlation of the Glyndebourne Hardgrounds and phosphatic chalks with those of Strahan's Hardground at Lewes and the stratigraphically similar Tilleul Hardgrounds of Haute Normandie. Recent excavations at the Cliffe Industrial Estate (Southerham Works Pit), have revealed the correlative surfaces for Glyndebourne Hardgrounds 1, 2 & 3, separated by the Malling Street Marls (see below). One of the higher Glyndebourne hardgrounds may, however, correlate with Strahan's Hardground. One of the probable results of the hardgrounds forming has been to occlude some of the marker marls (Lighthouse, Iford etc.) or cut them out entirely by channel erosion.

Glyndebourne Pit 1 is the only locality where phosphatic chalks of this age have been identified in England and their presence here is probably related to the tectonic development of the major structures in the area (Kingston Anticline – Caburn Syncline) and should be considered together with the unconformable relationships seen between the Gault - Glauconite Marl (Asham Pit 1) and Zig Zag Chalk - Plenus Marls (Machine Bottom, Southerham) and the Southerham Grey Pit Mid-Cenomanian Channel. In addition to the hardgrounds and phosphatic chalks, beds above Glyndebourne Hardground 1 are characterised by conglomerates of chalk intraclasts. Glyndebourne is considered to lie along a major tectonic 'hinge-line' which was probably operative during the Cretaceous (Mortimore & Pomerol, 1991b; Mortimore, Pomerol & Lamont-Black, 1996).

Locality 8. Glyndebourne Pit 2 (TQ 446105)

Summary of geological interest

New Pit Beds: Middle Turonian.

This small pit beside Week Lane contains the New Pit Marl 1 at the top of the main face. *Inoceramus lamarcki* (Parkinson) is found in beds below this marl associated with weak griotte marls. Several moulds of *Collignoniceras woollgari* have also been obtained from the same levels and one band of *Orbirhynchia* was found in the lowest exposures.

Locality 9. Bridgewick Pit (TQ 4311113)

Summary of geological interest

Lower Lewes Chalk. Southerham Marl 1 to Lewes Marl: Upper Turonian

It is uncertain whether Bridgewick Pit was included in the general group of Malling Street Pits by earlier workers, but this quarry has been used to establish the character of the Ringmer and Kingston Beds in the Lewes Chalk (Mortimore, 1986a). Bridgewick is now a Nature Reserve for birds run by Sussex Wildlife Trust and access is limited, especially in the breeding season.

The track leading to the pit crosses the poorly exposed Plenus Marls – Melbourn Rock contact. The pit is in the form of an amphitheatre with three faulted bluffs of well exposed chalk between the Bridgewick and Lewes Marls, but the sections can be extended downwards to the Southerham Marl particularly on the western side (Lake *et al.*, 1987, fig. 24, p.71).

In nodular beds beneath each of the Southerham, Caburn and Bridgewick Marls is an aragonitic fauna of *Bathrotomaria* sp. and *Scaphites* sp. *Lewesiceras* has been obtained immediately below Bridgewick Marl 1. In the marked nodular bed immediately below the here poorly developed Bridgewick Marl 3, heteromorph ammonites including *Alliocrioceras* and *Scaphites* occur. Two other horizons with gastropods (trochids and pleurotomariids) and scaphitids are found beneath the Kingston Columnar Flints and in the lowest of the upper three Kingston nodular chalk seams within the horizon of Lewes Flints. Moulds of ammonites some clearly related to *Lewesiceras* but others possibly to *Subprionocyclus,* occur beneath the Bridgewick and Lewes Marls.

Varieties of *Micraster* collected from this pit occur (i) beneath the Bridgewick Hardgrounds: *M. corbovis* of *lata* Zone type (Rowe, 1899; Stokes, 1977) [*Roweaster rowei* (Drummond, 1983)] associated with abundant *Sternotaxis [Holaster] planus* (Mantell); (ii) in a band above the level of Bridgewick Marl 3: *Micraster* of a *pre-leskei* form (Drummond 1983) and *Eomicraster corona* (Drummond ms, 1983); (iii) in the middle and upper Kingston Beds particularly in the lower belt of Lewes Tubular Flints: small *M. leskei* (Desmoulins; Stokes, 1977), the *Eomicraster leskei minor* of Drummond 1983; (iv) immediately below (often in burrow-fills) in and just above the Lewes Marl; large *M. leskei* or *Eomicraster leskei magna* (Drummond ms, 1983); (v) in the South Street Beds: *M. precursor* (pars sensu Rowe; Drummond, 1983) and a band of large forms possibly related to *M. corbovis* ss (Forbes) of *planus* Zone type.

The lower belt of Lewes Flints also contains horizons with *Cretirhynchia minor*

(Pettitt), *C. octoplicata* (J. Sowerby), *C. cuneiformis* (Pettitt), and *Orbirhynchia reedensis* (Etheridge), an assemblage indicative of the upper levels of the 'Chalk Rock' *sensu stricto.* In these expanded beds inoceramids of the *Mytiloides striatoconcentricus* (Gümbel) assemblage are common and continue into the South Street Beds.

Locality 10. New Pit, Malling Hill (TQ 424113) and **Malling Track** (TQ 423112)

Summary of geological interest

New Pit – Lewes Chalk contact: inoceramids and ammonites in the Middle and Upper Turonian.

New Pit exposes chalk from below the New Pit Marls in the New Pit Chalk to the Bridgewick Marl 1 in the Lewes Chalk. A very fine junction between the New Pit and Lewes Chalk can be seen in the air-weathered sections at the top of the quarry.

The sections are most easily studied by scrambling up to the eastern face to the first bluff (faulted New Pit Marls), and then working westwards across the main face which exposes, in succession, beds from the Glynde to Bridgewick Marls.

New Pit Marls are not easily located in the now overgrown lower part of the quarry but New Pit Marl 2 is exposed in the lowest bluff on the upper grassy slope of the eastern face. Several faults complicate the exposure though by shallow excavation with a hammer the New Pit Marl 1 can be found.

Above the first bluff is the beginning of the main face, at the base of which is the Glynde Marl overlain by a typical succession of 5 marls before the first nodular chalk seams are encountered. This excellent exposure of the Glynde Beds provides ample evidence of the entry of flints and nodular chalks characteristic of the Lewes Chalk and contrasting with the smoother, more massive New Pit Chalk below. The overlying key marker marls and flints (Southerham, Caburn, Bridgewick), form conspicuous grooves and grey bands across the face. Several faults can make instant identification of the marker beds difficult but the associations of particular flints and marls (Mortimore, 1986a, 1987) assists recognition.

The highest beds recorded here are the Kingston Columnar Flints in the Kingston Beds.

Several *Micraster* have been collected including *Roweaster rowei* (Drummond ms) from the nodular part of the Glynde Beds at the base of the Lewes Chalk.

The biostratigraphy is more easily studied on Malling Track to the west of New Pit. Marker marl seams are exposed in turn along this track from the New Pit Marl 3 to the Bridgewick Marl. Excellent examples of *Inoceramus cuvieri* and *I. apicalis* and bands containing *Romaniceras deverianum* and *R. (Yubariceras) ornatissimum* (Stoliczka) have been found along this track.

Locality 11. Malling Pit, Prince of Wales Pub (TQ 423108)

Summary of geological interest

Malling Street Marls to Southerham Marl.

The Prince of Wales Pub occupies the floor of the now overgrown Malling Hill Pit, figured by Mantell (1822, fig. 3). Temporary exposures on the slope where trees have been removed, have shown the position of the Malling Street Marls and in the highest part of the face (approached from Malling Track) the basal beds of the Lewes Chalk are still exposed.

On the road leading from the Prince of Wales Pub to the north portal of the Cuilfail Tunnel the New Pit Marl 2, Marl 3 and the Glynde Marl 1 are exposed at the base of the steep cliff at the east of the undercliff wall. A hurricane in October 1987 blew down many of the trees on this slope revealing the base of the Lewes Chalk (Figure 13). The upper New Pit and Glynde Beds were temporarily exposed in the old quarry into which the north portal of the tunnel was constructed.

Locality 12. Tarring Neville Quarry (TQ 445035)

Summary of geological interest

Seaford Chalk, Cuckmere Beds; Coniacian – Santonian boundary.

The ARTEX Quarry in Tarring Neville, near Newhaven, exposes the Cuckmere Beds in the Seaford Chalk between the Seven Sisters Flint Band and the trio of flints at the base of the Santonian (Michel Dean, Baily's Hill and Flat Hill Flints). The chalk is quarried for its purity which is required in the manufacture of ARTEX ceilings.

On the main face the thick (0.25-0.3 m) semi-tabular Seven Sisters Flint is present just above the floor of the quarry and is associated with the same inoceramid bands as seen at Birling Gap. A level of abundant *Volviceramus* ex gr. *involutus* (J. de C. Sowerby) is 1.6 m below the flint but volviceramids and abundant *Platyceramus* also occur with the two Cuckmere Flint bands above.

About halfway up the main face of the quarry is another conspicuous, sometimes semi-tabular flint (the Tarring Neville Flint). This is succeeded by soft, pure white chalks largely barren of fossils except for bands with sporadic *Micraster coranguinum* (Leske). The highest beds can be studied by taking the old upper roadway to the top of the quarry where there are excellent examples of *Cladoceramus undulatoplicatus* (Roemer) at the level of the Flat Hill Flint, which like the same level at Ramsgate and Kingsdown in Kent, the Bedwell's Columnar Flint, contains Paramoudra columns. Good specimens of other basal Santonian fossils can be found including *Gibbythyris ellipsoidalis* (Sahni), *Micraster bucaillei* (Parent) and typical *Isomicraster*.

There are several prominent north-south faults, wedging open towards the ground surface and infilled with sands and clay-with-flints in this quarry. These run parallel to the axis of the Ouse Valley and are thought to have been partially generated during the Quaternary.

One of the University of Brighton's research boreholes in the Ouse valley was drilled here to investigate the Chalk geophysical borehole log signatures. (The other boreholes were at Asham and Chandlers Yard, Lewes and were logged by the Southern Water Authority). The signatures proved, however, to be anomalous and though initially disconcerting, have subsequently supported structural and sedimentological interpretations showing a thick basin in the middle of the Downs between Lewes and the coast (Mortimore, 1986b).

THE SUSSEX COAST SECTIONS

Beachy Head and the Seven Sisters are the most famous Sussex coast sections but of equal geological interest are Seaford Head between Seaford and the Cuckmere, and the Newhaven to Brighton cliff sections. These form three day-long itineraries.

Itinerary 2. Holywell - Beachy Head - Birling Gap - Seven Sisters

Time and tide are critical on the long walk from Cow Gap (TV 597957) to Birling Gap (TV 553959) and tide tables should be consulted before attempting this itinerary. A falling tide is essential. It is also essential that the steps at Birling Gap are in place. Sometimes winter storms destroy these steps and they may not be replaced immediately. PLEASE CHECK THAT THESE STEPS ARE IN PLACE BEFORE SETTING OUT. It is possible to walk from Eastbourne railway station or catch a bus to Holywell kiosk by St. Bedes School, where cars can also be parked along the road. Buses also go to Birling Gap via Beachy Head.

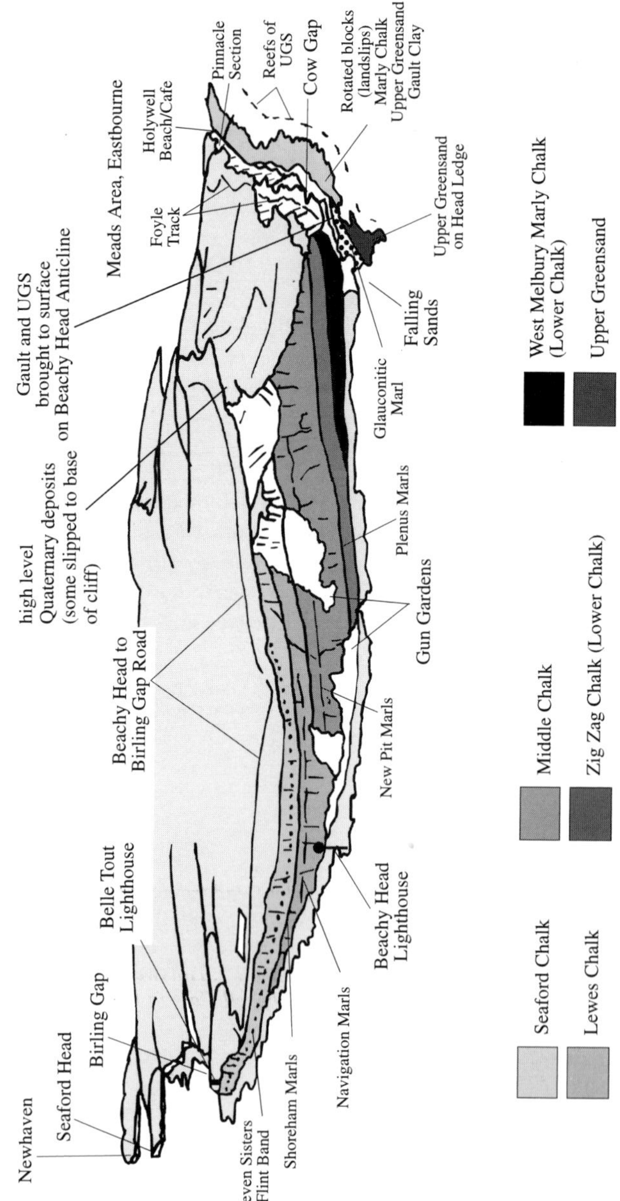

Figure 19. Aerial sketch of the Sussex Chalk cliffs around Beachy Head.

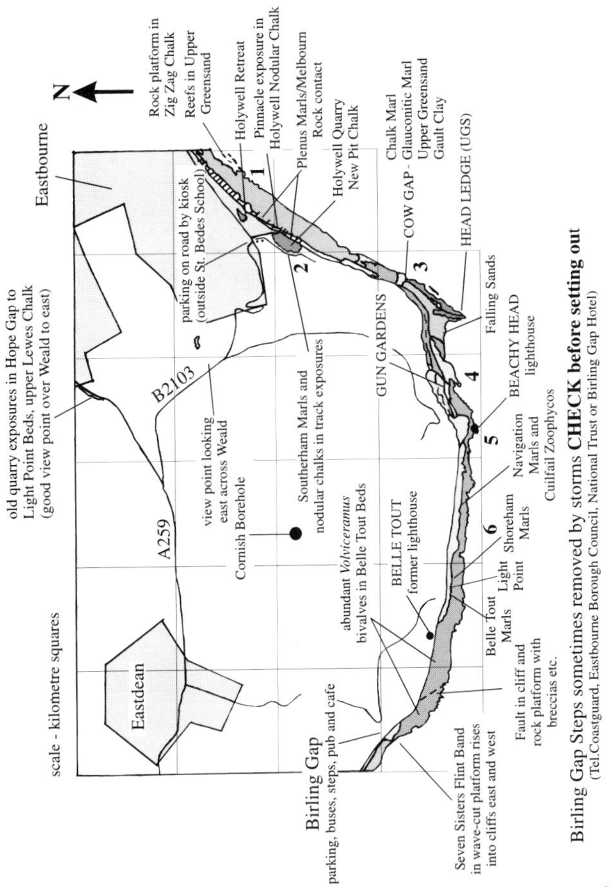

Figure 20. Map of localities around Beachy Head from Eastbourne to Birling Gap. Undercliff walk requires 6hrs (on a falling tide). Note steps at Birling Gap are sometimes swept away. The numbers, which are not Itinerary location numbers, refer to: 1. Holywell lower track to the Pinnacle and beach or from Holywell Cafe to Pinnacle Steps, at beach level – Plenus Marls – Melbourn Rock, Holywell Nodular Chalk. 2. Foyle track by telegraph posts; New Pit and Glynde marls and base Lewes Nodular Chalk to Southerham Marls. 3. Cow Gap: Gault Clay, UGS, Lower Chalk contacts; Quaternary slips and high level Quaternary Head slipped to beach level. 4. Falling Sands to Gun Gardens; UGS through Lower Chalk to Plenus Marls and Holywell Nodular Chalk. 5. Top New Pit and Lower Lewes Chalks with marker marl seams. 6. Top Lewes Nodular Chalk and base Seaford Chalk.

Locality 1. Holywell Sections and Foyle Track (TV 600968).

Summary of geological interest
New Pit Chalk – Lewes Chalk junction
(Middle – Upper Chalk boundary).

On the upper Holywell or Foyle Track to Cow Gap (Figures 19 & 20), the New Pit and Glynde Beds around the junction of the New Pit and Lewes Nodular chalks are exposed in a heavily faulted section. The telegraph poles at the Holywell end of the section are conveniently sited in relation to the New Pit and Glynde Marl seams. Beyond the telegraph poles, westwards, are beds rich in *Inoceramus cuvieri* (J. Sowerby) below and above the Glynde Marl, overlain by two prominent red, iron-stained, nodular hardgrounds containing large terebratulid brachiopods. These are the first of the Glynde nodular chalks at the base of the Lewes Chalk. The Southerham Marl, found halfway up the bank, above the nodular chalk layers, is associated with the typical Southerham Flints, the upper flint seam comprising tubular and finger flints and larger, nodular flints below.

A magnificent section in the uppermost Plenus Marls, the Melbourn Rock and the Holywell Beds is exposed on the lower Holywell track at the Pinnacle (Figure 21). This alternative route to Beachy Head requires much difficult walking along the shore. It can be approached either from the town end of the cliff to Holywell Cafe or from a track adjacent to St. Bedes School leading onto the top of the Pinnacle.

Holywell Cafe is at the southern end of the sea-wall promenade where Plenus Marls are partly buried in the flint-gravel beach, but the uppermost beds of the Marls (Jefferies, 1963), and the Melbourn Rock-Meads Marls-Holywell Marls are accessible in the cliff face (Mortimore, 1986a; Mortimore & Pomerol, 1995a). This section is repeated southwards to the Pinnacle Steps, where the Plenus Marls and top Zig Zag Chalk rise into the cliff. A feature here is the quantity of water thrown out along the cliff at the junction between the Plenus Marls and Melbourn Rock. This is exploited by the adits excavated into the Chalk at Holywell Pumping Station. The combination of relatively incompetent, thick Plenus Marls sandwiched between more competent Zig Zag Chalk and overlying Melbourn Rock has produced numerous open fractures in the stronger, more brittle beds.

The beach level Holywell sections and the Pinnacle Section provide the easiest access for measuring the basal beds of the Holywell Nodular Chalk. The Meads Marls are the most obvious markers, particularly the middle pair (3 & 4, Figure 21). In the air-weathered cliff faces the abundance of entire and fragmented inoceramids can be seen and many 'meso' fossils collected. The salt contamination unfortunately reduces the quality of the fossils which, for research purposes, are better collected from the inland pits at Southerham and Glyndebourne etc.. (Records of ammonites for this C/T boundary section will be particularly welcomed. They must be precisely located as one thin mm or cm bed may represent several metres of stratigraphy elsewhere).

Viewing the whole section from the railings (TV 600967) on the upper (Foyle) track, it is possible to fix the position of key marker marls at the base and in the Pinnacle and then trace the stratigraphy through the Eastbourne Water Works Quarry to the upper Holywell track. From here it is also possible to estimate the thickness of the Middle Chalk.

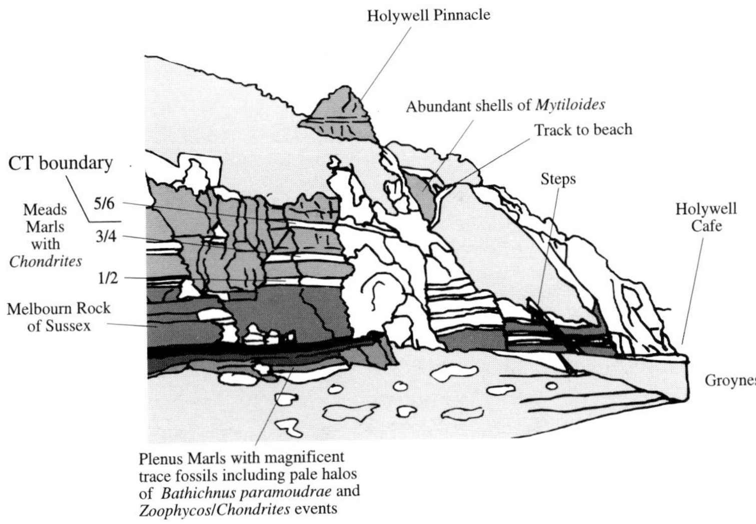

Figure 21. Sketch of the geology at the Holywell Pinnacle section, Eastbourne, looking northeast from near base of steps, the key Cenomanian – Turonian (CT) boundary section in southern England.

Locality 2. Cow Gap (TV 597957)

Summary of geological interest

Gault, Upper Greensand, Glauconitic Marl, West Melbury Marly Chalk.

The Cow Gap section is approached by the footpath across old landslips in the Chalk cliffs. Rotational slips have developed here by slipping of Chalk and Upper Greensand on the underlying Gault Clay and from the footpath (TV 596958) the complex pattern of slipped masses can be seen clearly in the wave-cut platform at low tide. The Upper Greensand forms off-shore reefs along the coast to Eastbourne as a result of the rotations. The section consists of a relatively undisturbed block of sediments within the landslips (Figures, 20 & 23) and is also described with some additional detail in the *Geologists' Association* companion Guide to the Weald, No. 55 (Ruffell, Ross & Taylor, 1996, Itinerary 5).

The topmost beds of Gault are intermittently exposed on the beach and exhibit a burrowed contact with the lowest bed of the overlying Upper Greensand, which consists here of a dark green glauconitic sand. Unfortunately, the contact is often poorly exposed. At this locality the precise position of the topmost Gault within

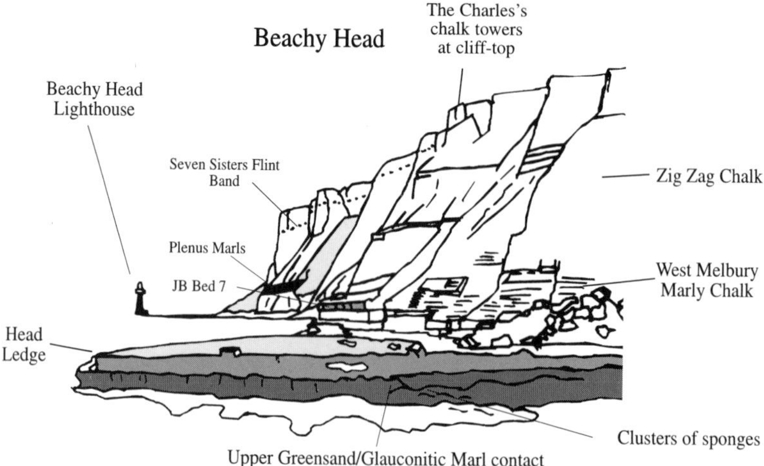

Figure 22. Sketch view of the Beachy Head (200m high) looking west from Head Ledge.

the Upper Albian zonal scheme is uncertain; the nearest diagnostic fossil recorded from this locality is a fragment of *Mortoniceras* cf. *inflatum* (J. Sowerby) found approximately 7 m below the base of the Upper Greensand and indicative of the *M. inflatum* Zone (Kennedy, 1967a). However, samples of Gault mudstone from 0.15 m below the Upper Greensand here have given micropalaeontological evidence of the *Stoliczkaia dispar* Zone (Davey, Medd & Wilkinson, personal communications 1977, 1978 via Young, 1980). (Records of *in situ* ammonites and other fossils are needed from this Gault/Greensand section, particularly from the Greensand).

The basal glauconitic sand of the Upper Greensand passes into very fine-grained, slightly micaceous calcareous sandstones in which occur several well-defined bands of calcareous doggers. These sandstones are well exposed both in the base of the low cliffs and on the beach and form the prominent reef known as Head Ledge (Figures 19 & 22). All these beds are strongly bioturbated, especially in the top 1.5 m below the Glauconitic Marl. Macrofossils are extremely rare. Jukes-Brown (1900) lists the following from the Upper Greensand at Eastbourne:- "*Nautilus* sp., *Kingena lima* [? *K. spinulosa* (Davidson & Morris)], *Pecten orbicularis* [*Entolium orbiculare* (J. Sowerby)], *Plicatula pectinoides* [*P. gurgitis* (Pictet & Roux)], *Holaster laevis* (Deluc) and *Jerea* sp." Though generally regarded as being of Late Albian age, Hart (1969) has suggested, on micropalaeontological evidence, that much of the Eastbourne Upper Greensand may be of early Cenomanian age. (Hence the need for more *in situ* fossils).

The contact with the Glauconitic Marl is not easily distinguished, though on close inspection it can be seen as an intensely burrowed surface with numerous crustacean burrows, including types referred to as *Thalassinoides* sp. (Kennedy, 1967b), that are up to 30 mm in diameter and penetrate as far as 0.65 m into the underlying sediment. Phosphatic nodules are common within the Glauconitic Marl and include phosphatised fossil fragments, fossil moulds and concretions some of which may have been derived from the Upper Greensand (Kennedy & Garrison, 1975). Well-preserved sponges are common here in the Glauconitic Marl which passes upwards into characteristically rhythmically bedded Lower Chalk in the adjacent cliffs. Non-phosphatised fossils from the Glauconitic Marl at Head Ledge include *Sharpeiceras, Mariella* cf. *dorsetensis* (Spath) and (Kennedy, 1969, p. 506) *Mantelliceras.*

In the West Melbury Marly Chalk cliffs immediately above the Glauconitic Marl at Head Ledge it is sometimes possible to measure and collect the section up to the limestone 'rib' and the bank of limestones with abundant *Inoceramus* ex gr. *virgatus.* These are the same limestone bands that were identified at Southerham Grey Pit (see p. 13).

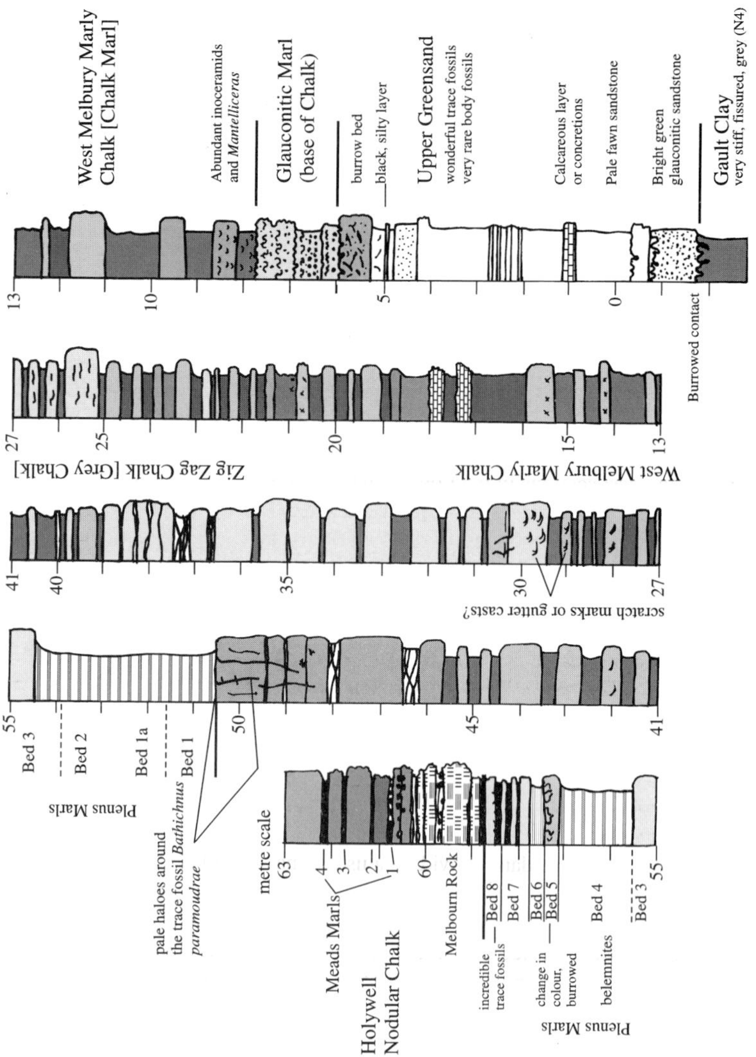

Figure 23. Geological section from the base of the Upper Greensand to the base of the Holywell Nodular Chalk at Beachy Head, Sussex. Bed numbers in the Plenus Marls refer to Jefferies (1963) bed numbers for the Plenus Marls. Bed 4 is the main belemnite bed.

The best sections showing the Gault, Upper Greensand, Glauconitic Marl and West Melbury Marly Chalk contacts are immediately below Cow Gap Steps and at the foot of the cliffs at Head Ledge to the southwest of the steps.

To the northeast of Cow Gap Steps are some excellent slipped sections in the West Melbury Marly Chalk showing horizons with phosphatic pebbles (Kennedy, 1969) from which zonally important ammonites have been collected (Gale, 1990). In the various Gault hollows between Upper Greensand reefs on the foreshore many eroded Gault fossils can be collected including several species of ammonites.

Locality 3. Falling Sands, Beachy Head (TV 593954)

Summary of geological interest
Glauconitic Marl to Plenus Marls sequence.

One of the best sections in the Lower Chalk of Southern England is found at Falling Sands where the whole sequence from the base of the Glauconitic Marl to the Plenus Marls can usually be studied if cliff falls are not too extensive. Of particular interest are the phosphatic and glauconitic pebble beds in the Lower Cenomanian marly chalk (Chalk Marl; Kennedy, 1969), the major lithological changes in the Middle Cenomanian and the distinctive 'scratched' lithology of Kennedy (1969) associated with large *Acanthoceras jukesbrownei* (Spath). (See Southerham Grey pit, p. 16, for discussion of the scratched lithology). The same fossil bands described at Southerham can also be seen at Beachy Head though the Lower Chalk is much thinner. The fresly wave-washed base of the cliffs usually reveals a very complex sedimentology of trace fossils in the grey-white alternations throughout the Lower Chalk. Cross-sections of large ammonites are common. In and below the laminated beds (*Zoophycos*), the brachiopod *Concinnithyris* is abundant, providing a useful marker in this part of the Middle Cenomanian.

Each bed can be collected in turn on the wave-cut platform when the tide is down. It can, however, be difficult to obtain accurate measured sections because of rock-falls and faulting. In addition to the macrofossils there is a stratigraphic distribution of trace fossils, many such as *Bathichnus paramoudrae* and *Zoophycos* recurring in abundance at specific horizons.

A feature of the Zig Zag Chalk here is its distinctly more rhythmic character compared to any other locality, particularly in the upper 10 m where *Holaster* is abundant. Another feature is the abundance of the trace fossil *Bathichnus paramoudrae* recognised by the pale columns of chalk in section and pale harder

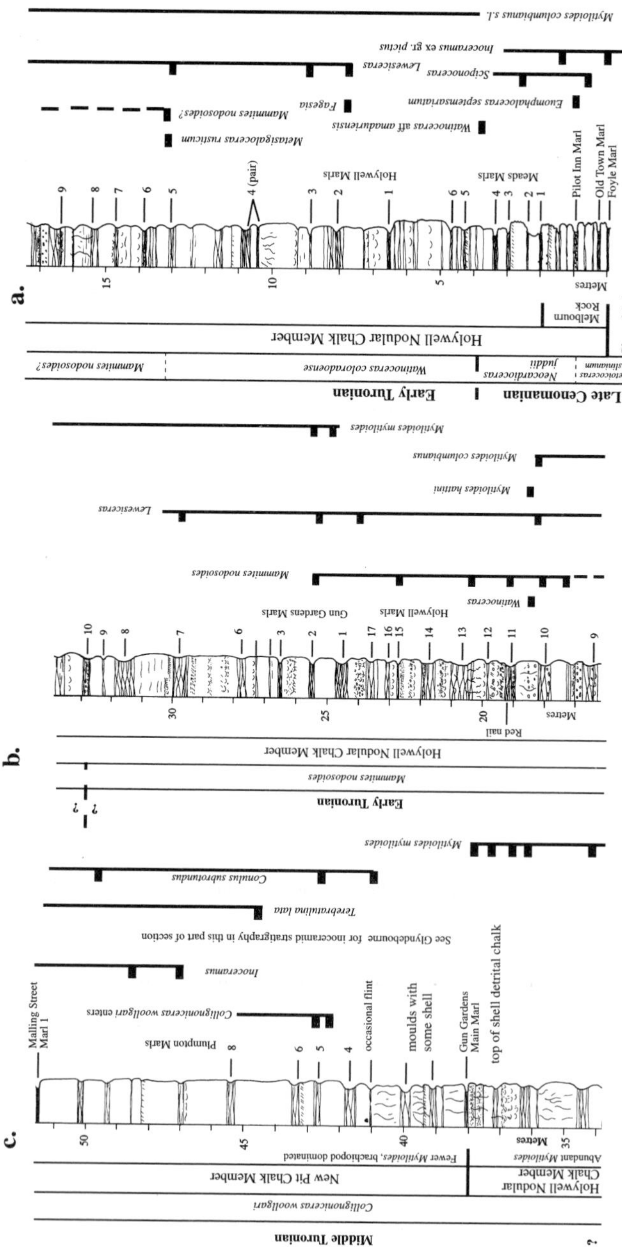

Figure 24. Geological section through the Holywell Nodular Chalk Member at Gun Gardens, Beachy Head. a. The Cenomanian - Turonian boundary and ranges of the more common fossils. b. Middle section of the Holywell Nodular Chalk Member containing the main Mytiloides *beds. c. Uppermost Holywell and Basal New Pit Chalk member and the change from* Mytiloides *shell debris chalks to brachiopod-dominated chalks with* Mytiloides *present mostly as moulds or very thin shells.*

circles in plan. Thin (1-3 mm), dark, sinnuous 'clay' cores are present in the centre of the columns and circles. This trace fossil is particularly well displayed on the surface eroded out of the base of the Plenus Marls (Mortimore & Pomerol, 1991b).

Locality 4. Gun Gardens (TV 587954)

Summary of geological interest

Plenus Marls, Melbourn Rock and Holywell Nodular Chalk Member.

Below the Charles's (the chalk towers or pinnacles at the crest of the 200 m high Chalk cliffs) there is a long steep grassy slope known as Gun Gardens (an old landslip that is gradually being eroded away). During Napoleonic times guns were mounted on the landslip, hence the name Gun Gardens. At the base of this slope is an excellent exposure of Plenus Marls and Melbourn Rock (Figure 23).

Jefferies (1963) described the Eastbourne – Beachy Head Plenus Marls sections, noting the great thickness here compared with anywhere else. His bed numbers are readily identified and the band containing the relatively abundant belemnite *Actinocamax plenus* is usually well exposed. The most obvious feature is the very thick dark grey marly chalk at the base containing abundant, sinuous, burrow-fill iron pyrites. Where the beds spread out on the foreshore a distinctive suite of trace fossils can be seen with each bed and the pale lumpy haloes of *Bathichnus paramoudrae* recur in the more limestone-rich layers.

Melbourn Rock

The Melbourn Rock of Sussex is expanded compared to most other localities, especially the type area of Cambridgeshire. As a result of this expansion, several key marker marl seams and nodular layers with associated diagnostic fossil have been identified (Figure 23) which are difficult to see elsewhere (e.g. North Downs). The top of the Foyle Marl is taken as the boundary between the Plenus Marls and the Rock (and the base of the Middle Chalk/Holywell Nodular Chalk) and is probably also the top of Jefferies' Bed 8 (1963). Fossils in the Chalk tend to occur at particular horizons (event beds). Both the main event horizons and the ranges of key macrofossils are shown (Figure 24). (For a definition of the Holywell Nodular Chalk and Melbourn Rock see Bristow *et al.*, In press).

Within the Melbourn Rock are pebbly (intraclast) nodular layers. Key fossil bands are used for correlation within the rock include two levels of abundant *Sciponoceras,* bands of abundant cidarid spines and bands of *Inoceramus* ex gr. *pictus.* (Records of *in situ* ammonites from this section are needed).

Above the Plenus Marls is an exceptionally thick Holywell Nodular Chalk compared to the sections outside East Sussex. The key marker marls are identified by the strong grooves in the cliff face (Figure 24). The conspicuous groove marking the Gun Gardens Main Marl usually comes down to beach level in sections immediately west of Gun Gardens and the base of this marl is taken as the boundary between the Holywell and New Pit Chalk members. This boundary marks the change from shell-detrital chalks below to smooth chalks above.

The Cenomanian – Turonian Boundary

The C/T boundary is of particular interest because of climatic and sea-level changes and stepwise extinctions of many taxa associated with the development of black shales (Plenus Marls – Meads Marls of the Anglo-Paris Basin, Black Band of Northern England and the North Sea), and marked geochemical spikes including $\delta^{13}C$, $\delta^{18}O$, manganese and iridium, generally held to be the result of the expansion of the oxygen minimum zone as a result of a period of global sea-level highstand which also led to climatic change. Thereafter throughout the remainder of the Cretaceous there was a general global cooling following a period of global warming. There are some similarities with the Cretaceous – Palaeocene (K/P) boundary. It has been necessary, therefore, to date the sections more precisely so that they can be correlated with world reference sections (e.g. Pueblo) and gaps identified by graphic correlation. In recent years, re-collection of the late Cenomanian and Turonian ammonites and inoceramids in the Sussex sections has considerably added to our knowledge of their biostratigraphy. Beachy Head has been shown to be the most complete C/T boundary section in the UK and Anglo-Paris Basin in terms of $\delta^{13}C$ and manganese signals (Gale *et al.*, 1993; Pomerol & Mortimore, 1993; Wood & Mortimore, 1995). In addition the microfossil ranges and ratios have been completely reassessed (Ferre *et al.*, 1996).

At Beachy Head, the late Cenomanian ammonites have included *Euomphaloceras septemseriatum* (Cragin) from the Pilot Inn Marl. *Inoceramus* ex gr. *pictus,* a Cenomanian species, is common in the Plenus Marls and Melbourn Rock up to the bed below Meads Marl 1.

The first *Mytiloides* are present in abundance between Meads Marls 4 and 5 and the entry of this genus is now taken as the base Turonian in this section. The microfossil records support this decision. Early Turonian ammonites include several bands of *Mammites nodosoides* and *Lewesiceras* which are now accurately located in the Gun Gardens section (Figure 24). The first band (Figure 24a) is associated with abundant early *Mytiloides* now referred to *M. columbianus*. A single specimen of *Watinoceras coloradoense* (Henderson) was found between Holywell Marls 2 & 3.

Great care is required when identifying key marker marl 5 in the wave-cut platform at Gun Gardens as several faults create difficulties. It is a very fine section for collecting ammonites and inoceramlds as each bed is exposed in turn over a considerable area.

Locality 5. Beachy Head (TV 583952).

Summary of geological interest

New Pit Chalk - Lewes Chalk junction
(Middle - Upper Chalk boundary).

A second, rather less steep, grassy slope opposite the lighthouse provides access to an outstanding section in the New Pit and lower Lewes Chalk and allows detailed study of the junction between these two members. Climbing towards the contact, the air-weathered New Pit Beds yield abundant fossils particularly *Inoceramus cuvieri* (J. Sowerby) between the New Pit and the Glynde Marls and a band of *Conulus subrotundus* (Mantell). Mesofossils are also abundant including small echinoids and brachiopods.

In this section the New Pit Marls are broad bands (200 mm thick) of brittle marl while the Glynde Marl is thinner (50-100 mm) but contains black plastic clays. The large deep water foraminife *Coskinophragma* is also evident in the weaker interlaced (griotte) marls beneath the Glynde Marl.

The base of the Lewes Chalk (and Upper Chalk) is taken at the base of the first nodular chalk layer rather than the Glynde Marl 1 as previously (in Mortimore, 1986). Glynde Marl 1 is overlain by a 2 m interval of chalks with marl seams, comparable to the New Pit section (see above). A remarkable series of weII-weathered nodular layers above the unit with marl seams is associated with the first regular flint seams. These are the same Glynde Beds nodular chalks seen earlier on the upper track at Holywell and the air-weathered fossils include *Sternotaxis [Holaster] plana* (Mantell) and *Micraster corbovis* of *lata* Zone type (Rowe, Stokes, 1975) as well as inoceramids related to *I. secunformis* (Heinz) and abundant *Terebratulina lata.*

The entry of nodular chalk layers gives the Lewes Chalk its characteristic lithology, representing a marked change from the more thickly bedded, uniform but marly New Pit Chalk. The nodular chalks form rhythmic layers repeated through the high cliff section to a point towards the top where more uniform white chalk begins (Seaford Chalk). This latter unit contains conspicuous fiint seams, the dark black line of the Seven Sisters Flint the most obvious (Figure 25a).

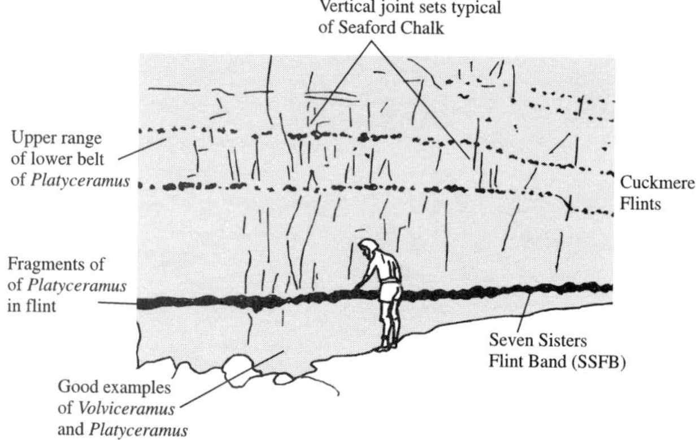

a. Seaford Chalk forming cliffs east of Birling Gap showing the continuous, semitabular Seven Sisters Flint Band. Dr. Richard Bromley for scale.

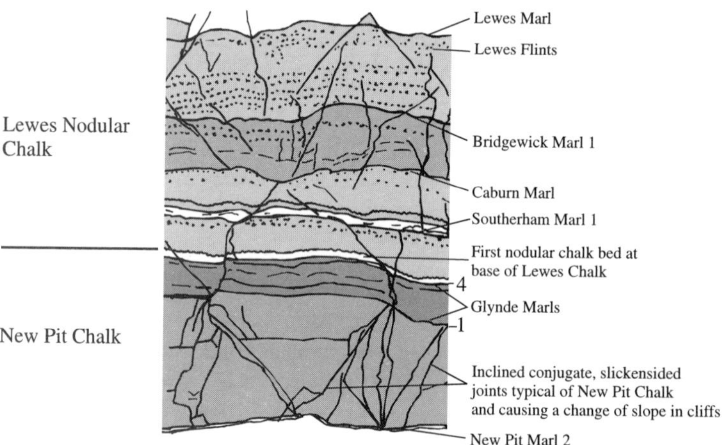

b. View of part of Beachy Head cliffs from the Lighthouse steps showing the contact between New Pit and Lewes Chalks.

Figure 25. Sketches of key levels in parts of the Beachy Head cliffs. a. The Seaford Chalk and the Seven Sisters Flint Band which rises to the top of Beachy Head Cliffs opposite the lighthouse. b. Key marker marl seams at the top of the New Pit and base of Lewes chalks. View from the lighthouse steps.

Locality 6. Beachy Head (TV 583953).

Summary of geological interest

Glynde to Navigation Beds succession: Upper Turonian.

Sections in the Chalk immediately north and west of the lighthouse provide lithological details in the lower half of the Lewes Chalk (Figure 25). Compared with Lewes, at Beachy Head the Bridgewick Marls and Lewes Marl are much less well-developed and the whole succession is noticeably thinner. Also the Southerham and Caburn Flints are more subdued compared to elsewhere in Sussex. This gives the impression that flints enter in strength at the level of the Bridgewick Flints, but this is oniy a local feature.

Other features are the *Bathichnus paramoudrae* traces which produce pale nodular 'haloes' in beds below the New Pit Marl 2, the intraclast conglomerates at the base of the Glynde Marl, the Lewes Tubular Flints either side of the Lewes Marl and the Cuilfail Zoophycos beneath the Navigation Hardgrounds. Selected levels such as the Navigation Beds demonstrate that individual layers between key marker horizons can also be correlated including flint bands, nodular layers and each layer of *Zoophycos.*

This section also illustrates the stratigraphic procedure adopted in the new lithostratigraphy. Although the Lewes Chalk, as a whole, is characterised by a succession of nodular horizons it was possible to further subdivide this Member into a useful series of beds based on units bounded by key marker marls. The basal surfaces of the Southerham Marl, Caburn Marl and Bridgewick Marl 1 are the boundaries between the Glynde, Caburn, Ringmer and Kingston Beds. The Marls, where possible, are chosen as the boundaries as these are the lithological layers most consistently developed and most easily identified throughout the basin. They were also the most easily identified features on geophysical borehole logs, the main source of sub-surface information in the Chalk.

It is difficult to be sure, but Rowe (1900), probably took beds well below the Navigation Hardgrounds (possibly Lewes Nodular Chalks) as the boundary between his *Sternotaxis [Holaster] planus* and *Micraster cortestudinarium* Zones at Beachy Head (Navigation Hardgrounds being his barren beds). *Micraster* has been reinvestigated by Drummond (1983) and his refined zonation is an indispensable aid to correlation of key marker horizons at this level

Locality 7. Westwards from Beachy Head (TV 581953).

Summary of geological interest

Upper Lewes Chalk, Navigation Marls to Shoreham Marls: Coniacian.

Walking west from Beachy Head, the gentle dip of the beds towards the Birling

Gap synclinal axis brings each layer in the upper Lewes Chalk to beach level Cliff falls cover parts of the succession but regular removal of the debris by the sea has allowed a complete picture to emerge over the years. Chalk between the Navigation Marls and the Shoreham Marls corresponds closely to the conventional *Micraster cortestudinarium* Zone and includes: (i) The carious, pink flints between the Navigation Marls; (ii) A network of squashed, branching *Thalassinoides* in the Navigation Marls; (iii) The conspicuous Cliffe, Hope Gap and Beeding Flints and marker marls in the same beds; (iv) Abundant *M. normanniae cordata* (Drummond, 1983) in the Cliffe and Hope Gap Beds associated with *Cardiotaxis cotteaui* and *Cretirhynchia subplicata* (Mantell); (v) The coarse calcarenitic chalks above the Hope Gap Hardground similar to those at Seaford Head but without the slump beds (Mortimore, 1987b). The whole upper Lewes Chalk is noticeably thicker than at Seaford Head; (vi) The three Light Point Hardgrounds that coalesce on a small mound at the promontory leading round from Birling Gap (TV565954). This promontory has been informally called Light Point as the old Belle Tout lighthouse is located here on the crest of the cliff; (v) A series of distinctive, red, iron-stained sponge beds and associated intraclast conglomerates, the Beachy Head Sponge Beds associated with abundant *Cremnoceramus crassus (Petrasechek)* [syn. *C. schloenbachi* (Böhm)] and *Micraster turonensis* (Bayle); (vi) *Zoophycos* in the Light Point and Beachy Head Beds.

Rowe (1900, p. 332) took the sheet flint (tabular flint of Rowe) between the Light Point and Beachy Head Beds as the junction between his *M cortestudinarium* and *M. coranguinum* zones. At Seaford Head, however, he chose the "closed marl seam" traceable because of the sharply overhanging cliffs (see Mortimore, 1987b). This is the upper Shoreham Marl, a persistent marker bed throughout much of southern England.

Locality 8. Belle Tout to Birling Gap (TV 563955 - 552960)

Summary of geological interest

Shoreham Marls to Seven Sisters Flint Band; Lewes Chalk - Seaford Chalk junction: high Coniacian.

The upper Shoreham Marl marks a major change in chalk sedimentation in the basin with the replacement of conspicuous red, iron-stained nodular chalks by much more uniform and pure white chalks containing prominent flint seams. This change in gross lithology also results in more uniform development of joint systems and fracture frequency.

Within the basal Belle Tout Beds of the Seaford Chalk, three further marls (Belle

Tout Marls) are present in the cliffs beneath Belle Tout Lighthouse. At Birling Gap the Seven Sisters Flint is in the wave-cut platform, but it rises into the cliff both to the east (Figure 25) and west (Figure 8) of Birling Gap illustrating the gentle Birling Gap Syncline. To the east the flint is cut by a minor fault along which extensive brecciation, solution and calcite cementation has taken place. These curious structures have an uncertain origin; similar and probably related structures are present in the chalk between Hope Gap and Cuckmere Haven beneath the loess deposits. Some are clearly related to re-cemented pipes exposed by cliff recession, whilst others may have a neotectonic origin.

Fossils associated with the Belle Tout Marls and the Seven Sisters Flint Band include (i) bands of abundant *Platyceramus* sp.; (ii) two rich bands of *Volviceramus* ex gr. *involutus* with Belle Tout Marl 1 and 1.7 m below the Seven Sisters Flint Band; (iii) sporadic *Micraster turonensis* present throughout these beds.

Immediately west of Birling Gap steps, blocks of chalk from some 10 m above the Seven Sisters Flint Band indicate the presence of a weakly glauconitised nodular sponge bed (the Cuckmere Sponge Bed). Barrois (1876) mistakenly took this bed and the Seven Sisters Flint as the equivalent of the Whitaker's 3 inch Flint and overlying sponge bed at Margate, which marked the junction between the *M. coranguinum* and *Uintacrinus socialis* zones. Rowe (1900, p. 330) recognised Barrois' mistake and referred to the beds as Barrois' "spurious tabular and sponge bed". The Cuckmere Sponge Bed yields *Aptychus* and abundant opalised plant fragments.

At the western end of the Seven Sisters the Belle Tout Marls and Seven Sisters Flint rise into the cliff providing excellent collecting in the Belle Tout Beds. The higher Seven Sisters extend the stratigraphy up to the crinoid zones in the high Santonian and fallen blocks yield typical fossils from these levels.

Birling Gap is a convenient end to the itinerary as buses run regularly back to Holywell and the pub and cafe are open all day for food and dririks.

Itinerary 3. Seaford Head

Locality 1. South Hill Car Park and viewing point (TV 506979).

South Hill Barn provides both a convenient car park and spectacular views across the Cuckmere Valley and along the white cliffs of the Seven Sisters within which the conspicuous dark line of the Seven Sisters Flint, dipping southeast towards Birling Gap, is clearly visible (Figure 26).

The path from the car park is east towards the Seven Sisters and divides at the cattle grid. The right hand path leads down to Hope Gap Steps.

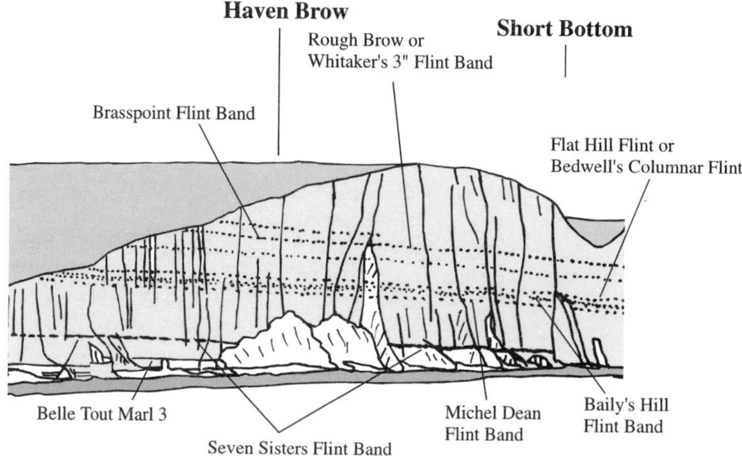

Figure 26. Sketch from a photograph of the first of the Seven Sisters. Haven Brow, looking east across the Cuckmere from Hope Gap, and showing the typical regular near vertical joint sets controlling the shape of the cliffs. Each major flint band in the Seaford Chalk is identified.

Locality 2. Hope Gap Steps (TV 509973).

Summary of geological interest

Cliffe and Hope Gap Beds (Lewes Chalk); Hope Gap Hardground.

On the foreshore and in the cliffs 20m west of Hope Gap Steps (Figures 27 & 28) are the Cliffe and Hope Gap Beds in the Lewes Chalk which here contain abundant *Echinocorys gravesi* and *Micraster.* Within the Hope Gap Beds these are mainly species recognised as early *M. decipiens* (Bayle) but also with forms comparable with late *M. normanniae.* In the Cliffe Beds the distinctive late *cordata* variety of *M.normanniae* (Drummond, 1983) predominates. This unit of the Cliffe and Hope Gap Beds is recognised as the *M. normanniae cordata* Subzone (Drummond, 1983) within the *M. normanniae* Zone. The upper surface of the Hope Gap Hardground is the boundary between the Hope Gap and Beeding Beds and is also taken as the boundary between the *Micraster normanniae* and *M. decipiens* Zones in this section.

The Hope Gap Hardground 20 m west of the “Steps” is the uppermost of a series of red, iron-stained nodular and hardground surfaces, and is overlain by a

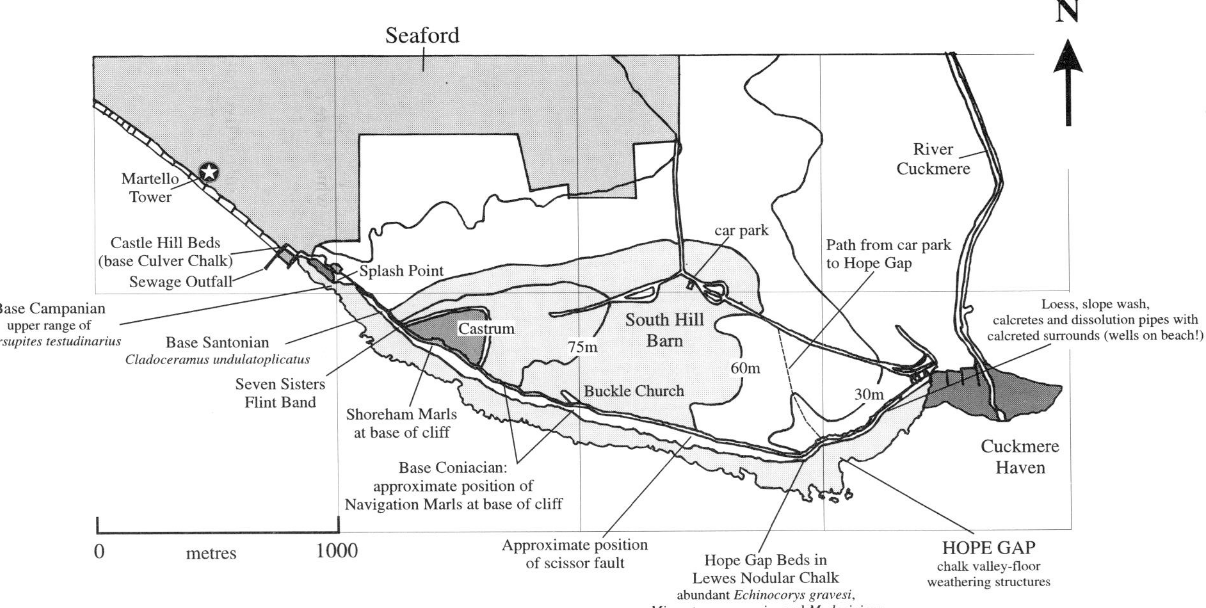

Figure 27. Map of Seaford Head showing the position of South Hill Barn (car park), Hope Gap and the approximate positions of key geological points along the cliff section. **(WARNING: only 1.5 hrs either side of low water should be allowed for getting around Splash Point. Access from the Seaford town end (west end) of the cliffs is across difficult concrete blocks and slippery timber groynes).**

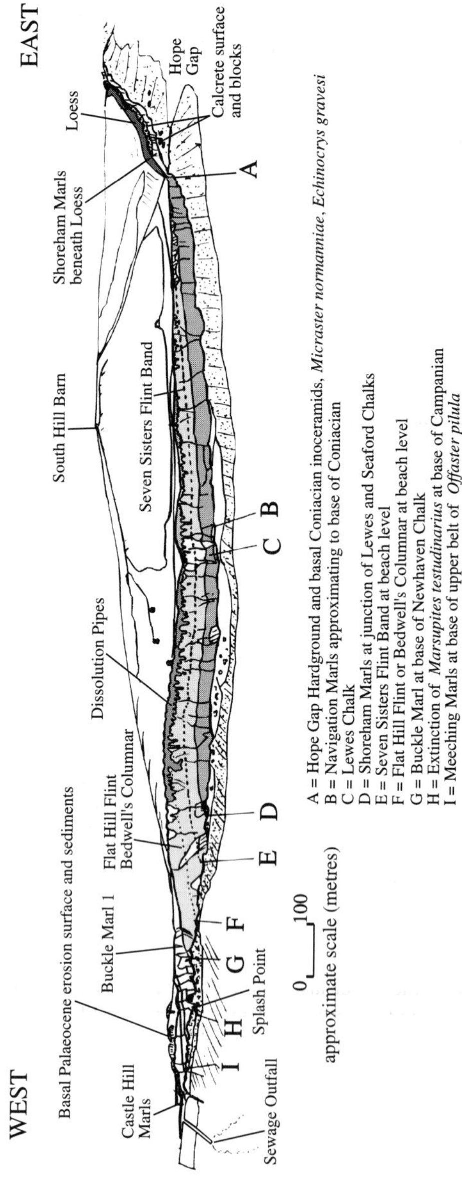

Figure 28. Seaford Head: a sketch from photographs showing the distribution of the major chalk units and marker beds.

conspicuous sheet flint. Above this sheet flint are 1.6 m of very soft, calcarenitic chalks with layers containing slump overfolds and 'laminae with shattered flints'. This unit is terminated by the 'streaky' Beeding Marl seam and contains the more inflated *'gibbous'* varieties of *M. decipiens* (Bayle) that characterise the base of the Zone.

The excellent wave-washed exposures allow the nodular chalks and hardgrounds to be studied in detail. Bromley (1965, 1967, 1975) has clearly demonstrated that such surfaces of hardening must have originated at, or close to, the sediment-water interface, as soft sediment burrowers in the sea-floor gave way to hard sediment borers and encrusters. The borings on the top surfaces of, and within, the nodular and hardground chalks, as well as the occurrence of encrusting oysters can be seen here. Small boring bivalves had also been obtained from the upper surface of the Hope Gap Hardground further to the west of the steps. Many phases of sedimentation and exhumation may be involved in the development of one hardground (Bromley records 16 phases of sedimentation in one hardground).

Hardgrounds are interpreted as the end member in a hardening process that started with discrete nodule development, but which eventually passed into a continuous bed of coalescing cemented nodules (Kennedy & Garrison, 1975). At this point on the foreshore the Hope Gap Hardground has a weakly glauconitised and convoluted upper surface, whilst hard, bored and glauconitised pebbles are also found in both the overlying sediment and in the hardground burrow-fill.

The Hope Gap Steps cliff section shows good examples of the commonly occurring alternation between a lower very grey, soft-chalk, and the overlying red, iron-stained nodular layers in which the grey sediment forms the burrow-fill A bed of chalk can, therefore, be divided into A (grey) and B (nodular) horizons, together forming a single unit or 'bed of chalk'.

The issue that attracts most attention, however, is the origin of the two main layers containing the slump laminae with shattered flint debris scattered through 'swirled' chalks. In the lower layer, nodules of flint have been ripped free, shattered and 'clumped' together, indicating considerable transport in some cases. There are sharp upper and lower contacts to each slump layer which also cross-cut burrows, thus clearly indicating post-depositional movement.

The upper slump unit, a soft calcarenitic chalk, contained three distinct layers exhibiting a form of 'pinch and swell', internal overturning, slump folding, and a degree of sorting of coarser debris. Each layer ranges in thickness between 10-100 mm. The uppermost layer contains small-scale slump overfolds and shattered flint and chalk intraclasts are clearly visible. The coarser debris tends to concentrate at the upper and lower contacts (bi-polar grading) and both contacts are sharp. The evidence for truncation of burrows again indicates that the structures post-dated sedimentation and early lithification. In some places early plastic-flow compaction faults and shears are found cross-cutting the beds, perhaps an indication of their early, post-sedimentary development (penecontemporaneous).

There is one intriguing small-scale chalk mound within the upper slump unit. Only 100-150 mm high and 20 mm in length as exposed in the cliff face, it exhibits an internally bipolar-graded structure. None the less coarser bioclastic debris appears to be concentrated at the base of the mound, and one shell fragment was found that penetrated the side slope of the mound; perhaps an indication of later compaction, or possibly evidence for relatively early formation of the structure.

The lower unit of slump bedding below the main group of Hope Gap nodular chalks shows an even more spectacular development of shattered and sheared flint shards, swirled around in what must once have been a highly mobile plastic chalk matrix. In some instances large *Thalassinoides* burrow-flints have been brought together in bunches, suggesting significant transport.

The theories on the origin of the structures in both units range from (i) primary sedimentary or syn-tectonic; (ii) penecontemporaneous movements; to (iii) post-depositional pressure solution.

There is a relative age sequence:

(i) First sedimentation, then early lithifications and flint formation, although silicification may not have reached the final chalcedonic stage.

(ii) Some confinement (i.e., limited overburden) when the layers were formed and therefore a post-depositional origin is indicated by the sharp lower and upper contacts of the layers; probable truncation of burrows at both contacts: fragmentation of the more brittle components chalk and flint); bi-polar grading of the fragments that suggest an upper and lower shearing contact during flow.

(iii) The layers are cut and offset by 'plastic-flow' small faults and shears (now annealed) of an early compaction type, perhaps indicating an early post-depositional origin.

Intra-Cretaceous intra-bed sliding seems the best explanation of the slump horizons, which possibly acted as layers of décollement.

The mechanisims for sliding could be (i) provided by sedimentary slopes, possibly tectonically controlled (i.e., early movements on the Seaford Head Anticline) and/or syn- or post-sedimentary tectonic thrusting or faulting; (ii) alternatively, transgression resulting in sudden greater overburden could drastically change the pore pressures in the poorly cemented chalk, reducing its shear strength and if already on a gentle slope, induce sliding; (iii) 'fluidisation' due to vibration of saturated sediment.

Some form of tectonic input or earthquake would seem to be necessary to overcome the shearing resistance provided by the embedded flints and to shatter them. These 'tectonite' layers could, therefore, be paleoseismic horizons. A clue to the mechanism and the timing of their formation may be found by a study of the 'surface-wear on the fragmented flint shards, as the surface texture should be different at the various stages of silicification from opal-CT to chalcedony. Studies of chalk textures using an electron microscope had shown considerable textural differences in the various 'tectonite' layers, possibly indicating differences in confining pressures during failure of the layers (Mortimore, 1979). Similar flint shard horizons associated with small-scale slumps and sheet flints are widespread in the South Downs at this stratigraphic level (e.g. Shoreham Cement Works, Adur Valley and Houghton Quarries, Arun valley) and the Isle of Wight.

Locality 3. Towards Seaford Head: Hope Gap Hardground fabrics (TV 504974).

Walking westwards towards Seaford Head, some general aspects of the geology can be examined. In contrast to the earlier plastic-flow and annealed shears, the more recent brittle failures such as minor faults, shear planes and joints can be seen controlling the modes of cliff failure. Standing back from the base of the cliff, there is a spectacular view of its 'castellated' sky-line caused by the weathering-out of deep solution pipes (Figure 29 and rear cover).

Stratigraphically, a similar level is maintained for most of the way, with excellent fossil collecting in the *Micraster normanniae cordata* Subzone and the overlying *M. decipiens* Zone.

The Hope Gap Hardground becomes more conspicous westwards and its extreme development is best studied at a cave cut along a scissor fault (Figure 27). Here, a rugged 300 mm thick bed of chalk with a highly convolute upper surface is strongly mineralised with green glauconite. The nodules show extreme development of a peripheral micro-crack fabric (Mortimore, 1979), perhaps further evidence of pull-apart due to sliding. Large inoceramids of the *Crennoceramus inconstans* (Woods) group have been collected from within the

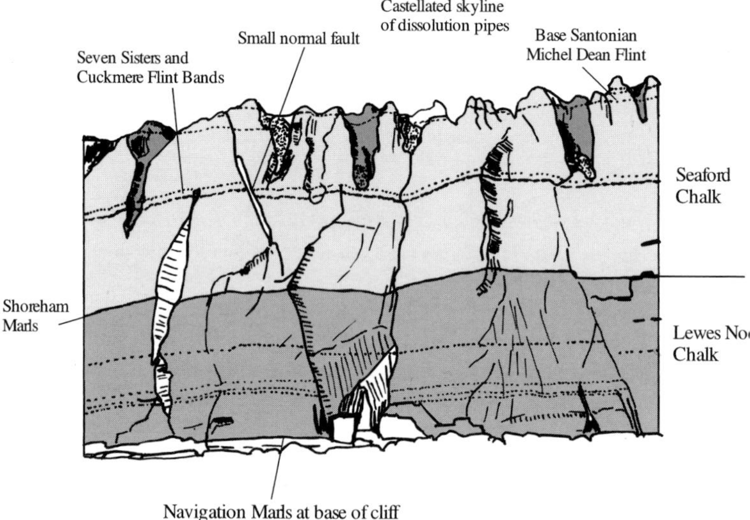

Figure 29. Sketch of cliff face below Buckle Church. Note inclined, slickensided fracture systems contrasting with the Seven Sisters, Fig 26. NB. Not all flints bands or flints within bands are shown.

hardground, while inflated forms of *Micraster decipiens* (Bayle) occur on the surface of the hardground.

Locality 4. The Sternotaxis (Holaster) planus Zone (TV 499975).

Further west, the effects of a normal fault and the slight easterly dip bring the Navigation Marls into view at the base of the cliff (Figure 30). These marls mark the approximate boundary between the traditional *Sternotaxis plana* and *Micraster cortestudinarium* zones. (As a result of great uncertainty created by the loss of Goldfuss' original specimens and their poor localisation the more unambiguously defined *Micraster normanniae* (Bucaille) and *M. decipiens* (Bayle) are used in place of *M. cortestudinarium* (Goldfuss)).

The two 50-70 mm thick Navigation Marls are 0.5 m apart and are associated with layers of intraclasts. The top surface of the upper Navigation Marl is taken as the boundary between the Navigation and Cliffe Beds. Beds below the marls yield *M. normanniae* ss. For the moment this same biostratigraphic boundary is taken as the Turonian - Coniacian boundary, although there is increasing evidence that this may occur around the level of the Cuilfail Zoophycos Beds.

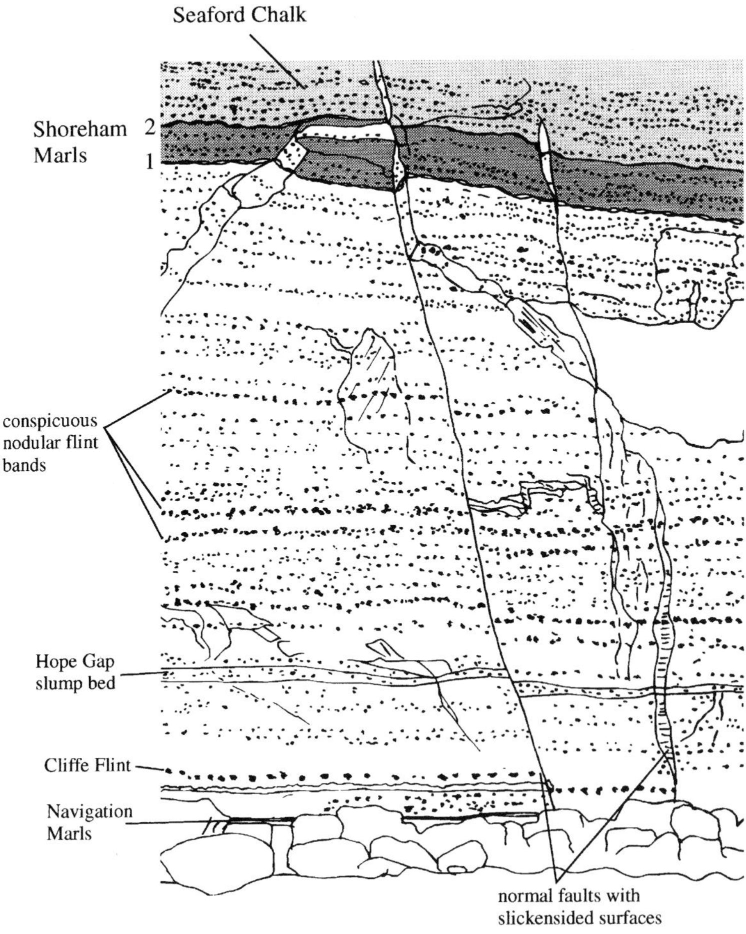

Figure 30. Sketch of the chalk stratigraphy in the lower part of the cliffs shown in Fig. 29 to the east of Buckle Church. The Navigation Marls at or close to the base of the Coniacian are at the very base of the cliff followed by several conspicuous marker flint bands in the upper Lewes Chalk.

Locality 5. Seaford Head: termination of the Hope Gap Hardground and Beachy Head Zoophycos Beds (TV 495977).

Continuing westwards, it is possible to see how the numerous nodular chalk surfaces are progressively cut-out by condensation beneath the Hope Gap Hardground as the sequence thins. At Seaford Head the Hope Gap Hardground (or an equivalent surface) is difficult to define for it is abruptly terminated and replaced by soft chalks containing a myriad of veins, probably due to sliding and pull-apart.

In addition to the Hope Gap Hardground structures, there are several layers of intraclast-conglomeratic chalk in the Beeding and Light Point Beds. Many of these layers appear to have no sharp upper contacts and are probably primary in origin.

Locality 6. Seaford Head (TV 494977)

Summary of geological interest

Shoreham Marls, Belle Tout Marls, Seven Sisters Flint Band (high Coniacian); Coniacian - Santonian Boundary; Haven Brow Beds (low Santonian).

In large fallen slabs of chalk from the Light Point and Beachy Head Sponge Beds the trace fossil *Zoophycos* is abundant and occurs as a post-omission suite of traces within the fills of earlier *Thalassinoides* burrows. (Post-omission = means after the omission surface, represented by the nodular chalk, has formed and has become buried by renewed sedimentation). The concentration of certain types of trace fossil at specific levels may indicate wide-scale changes in oceanography such as depth. This horizon of *Zoophycos* has provided a conspicuous correlation marker band in cored boreholes from the Thurrock area, Essex (Mortimore, Roberts & Jones, 1990), beneath London and across the Paris Basin. Numerous large shells of *Cremnoceramus crassus* are also found in the Beachy Head Sponge Beds.

At the base of the cliff below the Castrum at Seaford Head (Figure. 27) the two conspicuous Shoreham Marls are present (Figure 31a). Rowe (1900, p. 332) had noted the usefulness of the upper "closed marl-seam" in particular, forming a distinctive ledge in the cliff-face as it rises eastwards. Rowe took these marls as his boundary between the traditional *M. cortestudinarium* and *M. coranguinum* zones.

These Shoreham Marls and the Shoreham Tubular Flints have great lateral continuity (e.g. Thurrock and Faircross borehole cores) and therefore provide most useful lithostratigraphic markers. Layers of red, iron-stained nodular chalks are common up to these marls, and similar bands are sometimes found in the

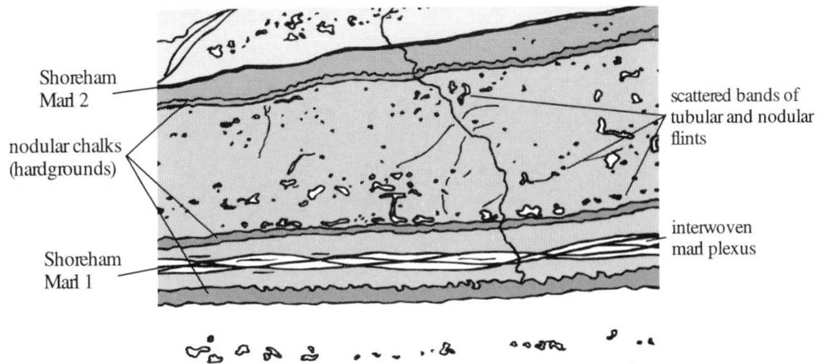

a.

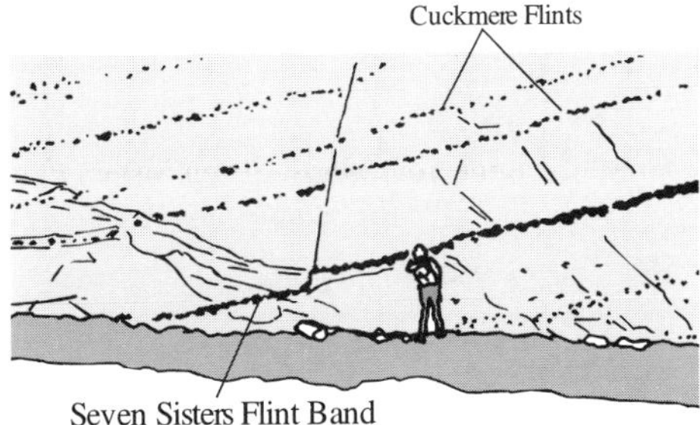

b.

Figure 31 a. Sketch of the Shoreham Marls and Shoreham Tubular Flints at beach level at Seaford Head. The tubular flints form a distinctive brash in ploughed fields and are conspicuous in core and field sections and used to assist mapping the Lewes – Seaford Chalk boundary. b. Sketch of the Seven Sisters Flint Band (SSFB) and Cuckmere Flint Bands (CMF) at Seaford Head dipping north on the Seaford Head Anticline. Scale given by figure (Steve Flitton, nearly 2 m tall).

3-5 m above. The top surface of the upper Shoreham Marl is now taken as the boundary between the nodular and flinty Lewes Chalk and the much purer, softer and featureless, flinty Seaford Chalk.

At this stage in the itinerary it is prudent to check the state of the tide and ensure that Splash Point can be rounded. **If the point cannot be rounded and the tide is rising then a quick retreat to Hope Gap Steps is absolutely imperative.**

The three Belle Tout Marls (see Birling Gap above), return to beach level in

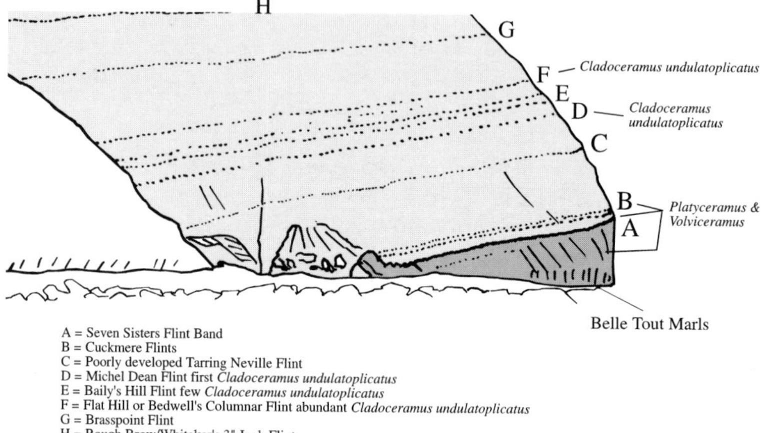

Figure 32. Sketch showing the position of the Seven Sisters Flint Band in relation to the Michel Dean, Baily's Hill, Flat Hill, Brasspoint and Rough Brow flint bands in the Upper Coniacian and Lower Santonian.

sight of Seaford. These and the Shoreham Marl 5 have also been identified along the Kent coast between St. Margaret's Bay, Hope Point and Kingsdown, in the Thurrock (Essex) and Faircross (Berks) boreholes, and at Whitecliff, Isle of Wight. An abundance of particular inoceramids, *Platyceramus* and *Volviceramus*, confirms identification and correlation of these marls.

Within the Seaford Chalk the most conspicuous markers are provided by a series of semi-tabular flint seams. By far the most prominent is the Seven Sisters Flint (Figures 31b & 32). The northerly dip brings the Flint to the base of the cliff just west of the Castrum (TV 493978) and here the over-silicified *Thalassinoides* burrow network gives the flint a vermiform top surface. The seam varies between 200-300 mm in thickness and contains patches of red iron-staining and sponges. Forms of *Volviceramus* ex gr. *involutus* (J. Sowerby), occur in abundance in a band 1.6 m below the Flint.

The top surface of the Seven Sisters Flint is taken as the boundary between the Belle Tout and Cuckmere Beds. In practice, especially core-logging, because flints are destroyed by coring, this boundary is taken at the last level of abundant *Platyeramus* fragments which occurs between the Cuckmere Flints. The Cuckmere Beds are conspicuously less fossiliferous, containing rather pure white chalks without many prominent features (the Barren Beds of core-logging, Mortimore, 1990). One of the two soft, nodular, red iron-stained sponge beds towards the top of these Beds is "Barrois' Spurious Sponge Bed" (see Birling Gap, p.55).

A conspicuous group of three bands of almost semi-tabular flints (Michel Dean, Baily's Hill and Flat Hill Flints) occurs towards the middle part of the traditional *M. coranguinum* Zone in Sussex and these are at beach level some 50 m west of the Seven Sisters Flint Band (Figures 32 & 33). The top surface of the lowest of this trio (Michel Dean) is taken as the boundary between the Cuckmere and Haven Brow Beds and this Flint is also the currently accepted boundary between the Coniacian and Santonian Stages (Figure 34). The entry of the key index fossil for this Stage boundary, *Cladoceramus undulatoplicatus* (Roemer) with its conspicuous corrugated ribbing, has been seen on the top surface of the flint.

GAFig.33

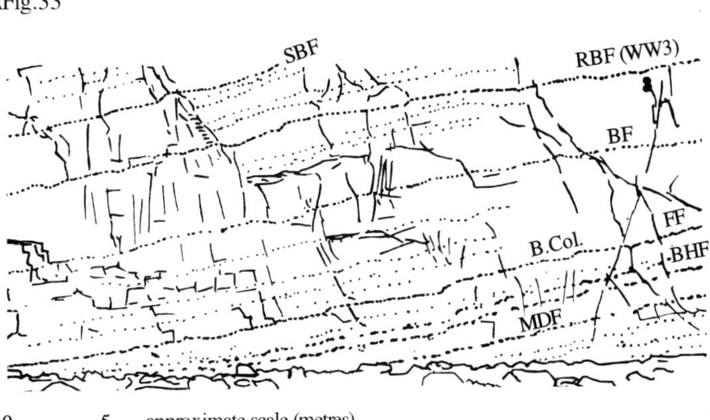

MDF=Michel Dean Flint; BHF=Baily's Hill Flint; FF/B.Col.=Flat Hill Flint/Bedwell's Columnar Flint; BF=Brasspoint Flint; RBF/WW3 =Rough Brow Flint/Whitaker's Three Inch Flint Band; SBF=Short Brow Flint.

Figure 33. Sketch showing the position of the key upper Seaford Chalk flint bands at Seaford Head, position F on Fig. 28. The base Santonian section, a World Reference Section.

Sporadic *Cladoceramus* occur with the Baily's Hill Flint but it reaches its maximum abundance in and above the Flat Hill Flint. Because of this association, and the presence of 'Paramoudra columns', this flint is correlated with the 'Bedwell's Columnar' of the Kent coast. Paramoudra columns also occur with the lower two flints and so, on their own, such flints could not be a rigid guide for exact correlation.

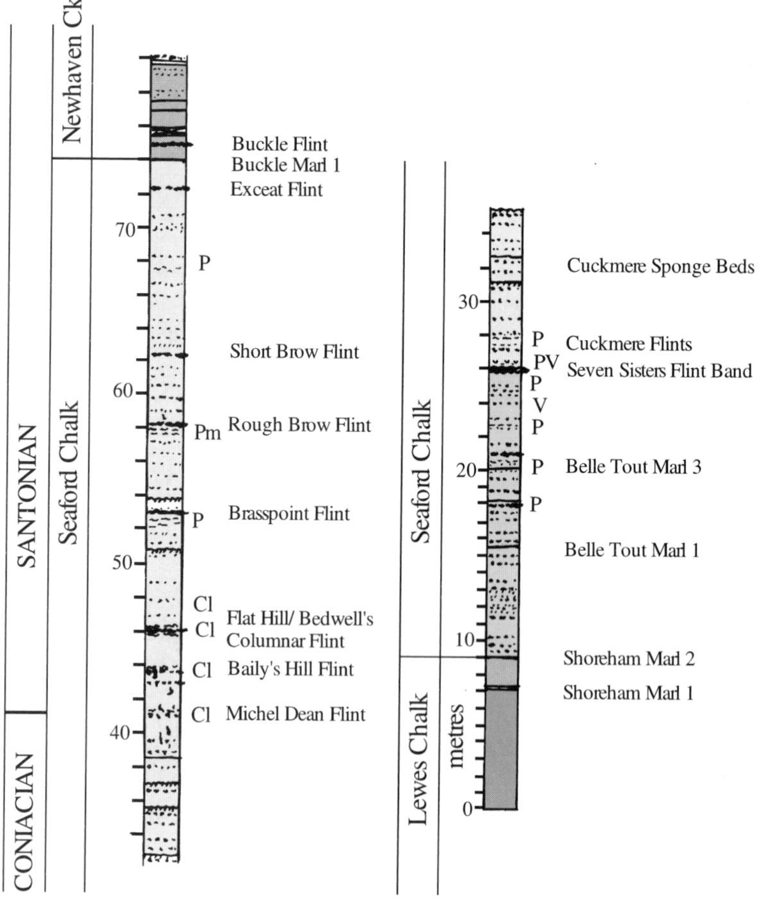

Figure 34. Stratigraphic log of the Seaford Chalk (Coniacian to Santonian) at Seaford Head (stratotype section). P= common Platyceramus *fragments, V = common* Volviceramus, *Cl = common* Cladoceramus undalatoplicatus.

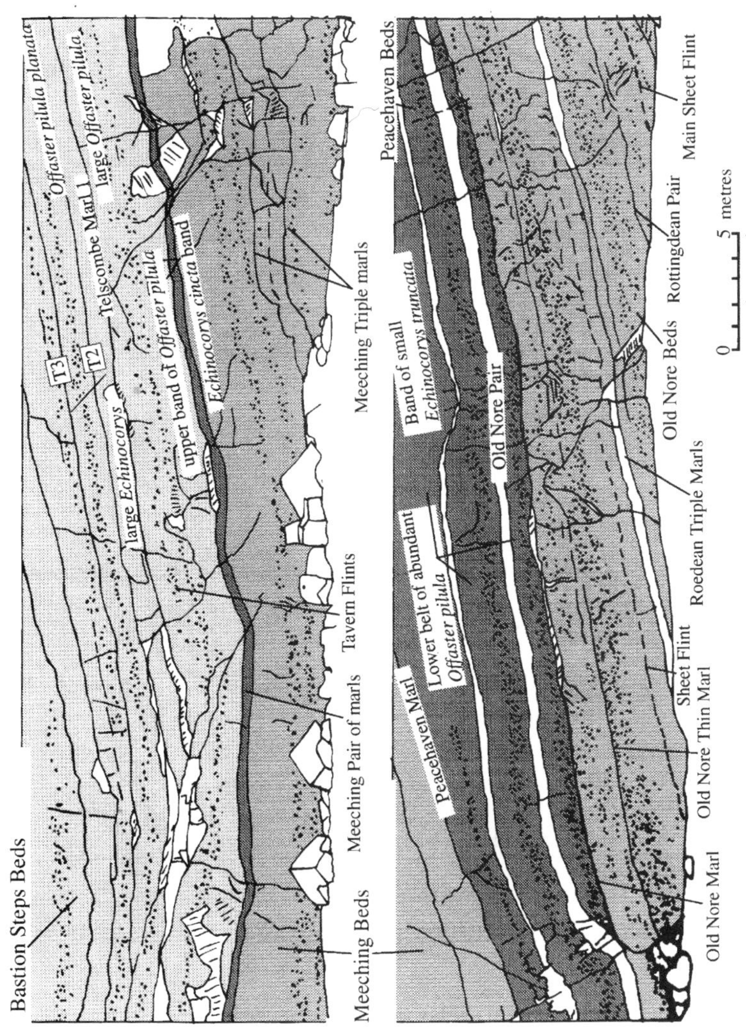

Figure 35a. Sketches from photographs of the Newhaven Chalk at beach level just east of Seaford eastern groynes. The chalk bedding is picked out by the dip 8°-10° north of marl seams and flint bands on the northern limb of Seaford Head Anticline. The sections a. continue into the section b (over page).

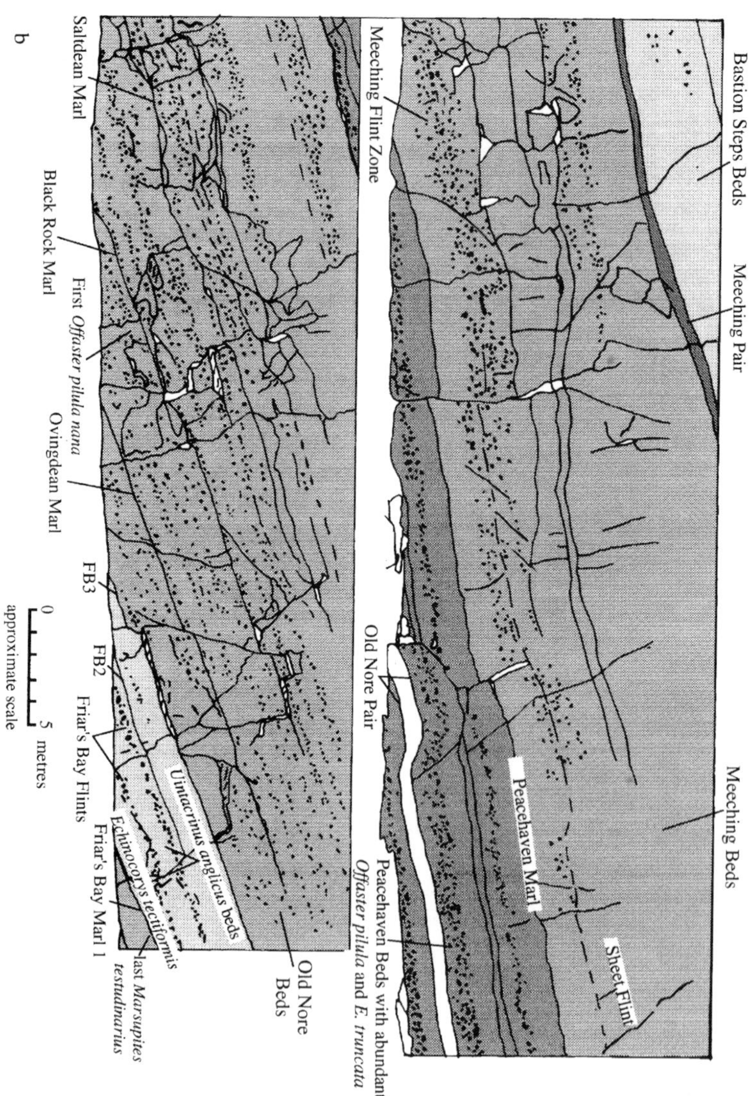
b
Saltdean Marl
Black Rock Marl
First Offaster pilula nana
Ovingdean Marl
FB3
FB2
Friar's Bay Flints
Friar's Bay Marl 1
Uintacrinus anglicus beds
Echinocorys tectiformis
last Marsupites testudinarius
Old Nore Beds
0
5 metres
approximate scale
Meeching Flint Zone
Old Nore Pair
Peacehaven Beds with abundant Offaster pilula and E. truncata
Peacehaven Marl
Sheet Flint
Meeching Beds
Meeching Pair
Bastion Steps Beds

Figure 35b

Four other conspicuous semitabular flints occur within the Cuckmere Beds (Figure 33): (i) the Brasspoint Flint, associated with abundant *Conulus albogalerus* (Leske); (ii) the Rough Brow Flint, associated with abundant *Platyceramus* and sporadic *Cordiceramus* and, therefore, equated with the Whitaker's Three Inch Flint of Kent; (iii) the Short Brow Flint, generally barren of fossils; (iv) and finally, the Exceat Flint, which is the lower of Rowe's (1900) "two flints 9 ft apart" at the base of the *Uintacrinus socialis* Zone (the Buckle Flint in the overlying Splash Point Beds is the upper of Rowe's flints).

Micraster coranguinum ss (Leske) is characteristic in this interval as well as *Isomicraster gibbus* (Lamark), particularly towards the base of these beds. (Belemnites and ammonites in the Seaford Chalk in Sussex are exceedingly rare. If you find any please report them and their exact location).

Locality 7. Splash Point (TV 491981).

Summary of geological interest

Base of the Newhaven Marly and Flinty Chalk; Splash Point Beds: *Uintacrinus socialis & Marsupites testudinarius* zones: high Santonian: Santonian - Campanian Boundary.

The return of marl seams in the crinoid zones (*Uintacrinus* and *Marsupites*) is a lithological change maintained throughout much of southern England (except in Kent) and is used to distinguish the Newhaven Chalk from the Seaford Chalk (Mortimore & Pomerol, 1987; Bristow *et al.*, in prep). At Seaford Head this junction is often seaweed-covered in the summer (winter storms usually clean the section). Buckle Marl 1 is a strongly developed griotte seam and its base is taken as the boundary between the Newhaven and Seaford Chalk Members and the base of the Splash Point Beds, as well as the base of the *Uintacrinus socialis* Zone. The remaining Buckle Marls are accessible in the various caves that lead round to Splash Point (TV 490981; Figures 27 & 36) in the floors of the caves the nodular beds are full of large ammonites (*Parapuzosia*). It is the concentration of particular fossil bands that makes this section exciting to study, particularly forms of *Echinocorys, Cretirhynchia, Bourgueticrinus,* and *Uintacrinus* (Mortimore, 1986). A number of marl seams form conspicuous grey bands in the cliff and the top surface of the most prominent, the Brighton Marl, is taken as the boundary between the Splash Point and Old Nore Beds (Figure 36). On rounding Splash Point beds including the Brighton Marl and up to the Friars Bay Mains are usually free of beach gravel and yield numerous fossils including

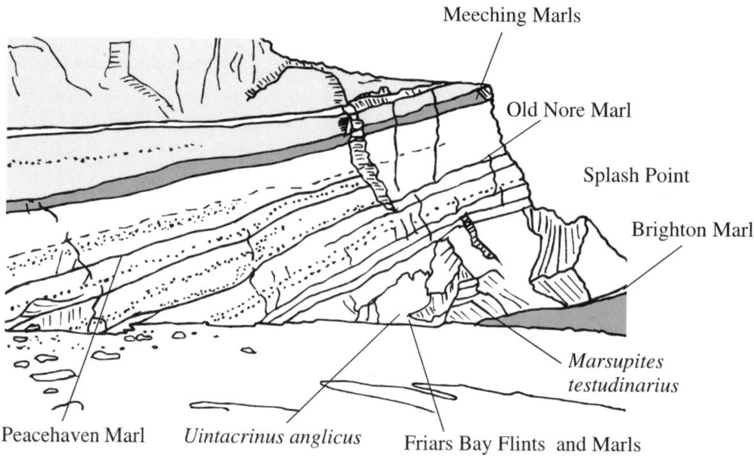

Figure 36. Sketch of Seaford Head, looking east from the old sewer groyne at Seaford. Only the position of key marker beds is shown.

Marsupites testudinarius (Schlotheim), various forms and sizes, three bands of *Echinocorys elevata* (Brydone), *Echinocorys depressula* (Brydone) associated with *Conulus* and *Micraster* in a bed below the Friars Bay Marl 1.

In the corner cave at Splash Point (Figures 35b & 36), are two conspicuous nodular, horn-flint seams (Friars Bay Flints) immediately above the Friars Bay Marl 1. These flints mark the horizon containing the elusive *Uintacrinus anglicus* band. It is not an easy fossil to collect or identify. The top of the range of the more readily identifiable *Marsupites testudinarius* is generally regarded as the boundary between the Santonian and Campanian in European chalk facies where the index ammonites are absent.

Locality 8. West of Splash Point (TV 490980).

Summary of geological interest

Newhaven and Culver Chalk Members.

The remaining beds above the Friars Bay interval in the higher Newhaven Chalk are illustrated in detail (Figure 35). Access to these levels is not so tide dependent, but care is needed when climbing across the concrete blocks and the seaweed covered concrete leading to the beach. Scrambling on these blocks is potentially ankle-breaking and should be undertaken with great care. The route down to beach level is slippery and hazardous.

Of particular note are the Peacehaven Beds which have at their base the best developed marl in the Newhaven Chalk (Old Nore Marl = Brydone's Three Inch Marl). The top of the marl is taken as the boundary between the beds and this is also the concentration of the lower belt of abundant *Offaster pilula* (Lamarck) associated with *Echinocorys truncata* (Brydone). A large ammonite, associated with intraclast conglomerates, from the upper part of these beds had encrusters attached to the 'chalk' infill rather than the shell, and the encrusters were on the underside, suggesting that the heavy, chalk-filled ammonite had been ripped-up, transported and re-buried, an indication of powerful currents or slumping on the chalk sea bed. The paleomagnetic reversal from 34Normal to 33Reverse has been identified as occurring in the bed below the Old Nore Marl (Pascal, 1995).

In the overlying Meeching and Bastion Steps Beds the boundary marls between the divisions are the upper surfaces of the Peacehaven and the upper Meeching Marl respectively (Figure 35a). Telscombe Marl 1 with its intraclast pebble conglomerate is also a key marker. *Offaster pilula* (upper belt) and the larger *Offaster pilula planata* (Brydone MS Ernst) are found in the beds above the Meeching pair.

On the last scramble over the groynes onto the sewage outfall (TV 488982), the uppermost Bastion Steps and the Castle Hill Beds are exposed. The base of the Castle Hill Beds (also the base of the Culver Chalk Member) is taken along the top surface of the last marl in the section, the upper Castle Hill Marl. The Culver Chalk, like the Seaford Chalk, is largely free of marl seams and layers of nodular chalk but contains conspicuous flint seams. Eleven Castle Hill Flints and associated *Echinocorys* bands are in the section adjoining the undercliff walk. Looking back on the section from this vantage point, the dip 10° north on the Seaford Anticline is obvious and is responsible for providing the exposures of such a complete stratigraphy in the Chalk. Each marker marl seam in the Newhaven Chalk weathers to a pale band in the cliffs.

Belemnites are much rarer in Sussex than similar levels in Kent and Wessex and any ammonites or belemnites found will be valuable records.

Itinerary 4. The coast sections from Newhaven to Brighton.

The Newhaven to Brighton coast section can be walked in a day and is very rewarding for those interested in echinoids from Chalk not present in the North Downs, the basal Tertiary sediments and Quaternary periglacial(?) processes. The west side of Newhaven harbour is a suitable starting point and a falling tide is recommended so that the chalk wave-cut platform can be investigated *en route* to Brighton. Alternatively, a series of vehicle stops can be made between Newhaven and Brighton. The entire cliffs from Newhaven to Brighton is a geological SSSI but there are special features at Newhaven, Portobello and Black Rock.

Locality 1. Castle Hill (TQ 445000) **to Old Nore Point** (TV 435998).

Summary of geologieal interest

Newhaven and Culver Chalks: *Offaster pilula* and *Gornoteuthis quadrata* zones: Lower Campanian: Tertiary sediments.

Extensive parking is available in the NCP car park on the western arm of Newhaven Harbour. Easiest access to the cliff face is west of the car park. This can be approached either by walking from Newhaven Railway Station, across the swing bridge over the Ouse, past Newhaven Marina to the Castle Hill Cliffs or by taking a left turn at the Police Station off Newhaven's one way traffic system and following the sea-front signs to Castle Hill Cliffs.

Access to the Tertiary exposure can either be via the steep gully (Figure 38) visible in the cliffs (very, slippery and muddy in wet conditions) or via the old fort and coastguard lookout. This latter route requires a walk back along the road towards Newhaven then a turn to the west following the signs to the fort.

Patches of Tertiary sediments are preserved along the southern edges of the South Downs (Figure 37) and in synclines such as the Caburn Syncline at Falmer. Many of these patches are highly disturbed and weathered (foundered Tertiaries of local British Geological Survey Memoirs). At Newhaven, a relatively undisturbed patch of Tertiary (Figure 38) provides an invaluable insight to these otherwise very poorly exposed deposits in the Sussex Downs. The sub-Tertiary erosion surface is irregular with some shallow-sided erosional and karst features. Some dissolution pipes of various sizes are present but whether this is a sub-Paleocene karstic surface like Alum Bay (Isle of Wight)

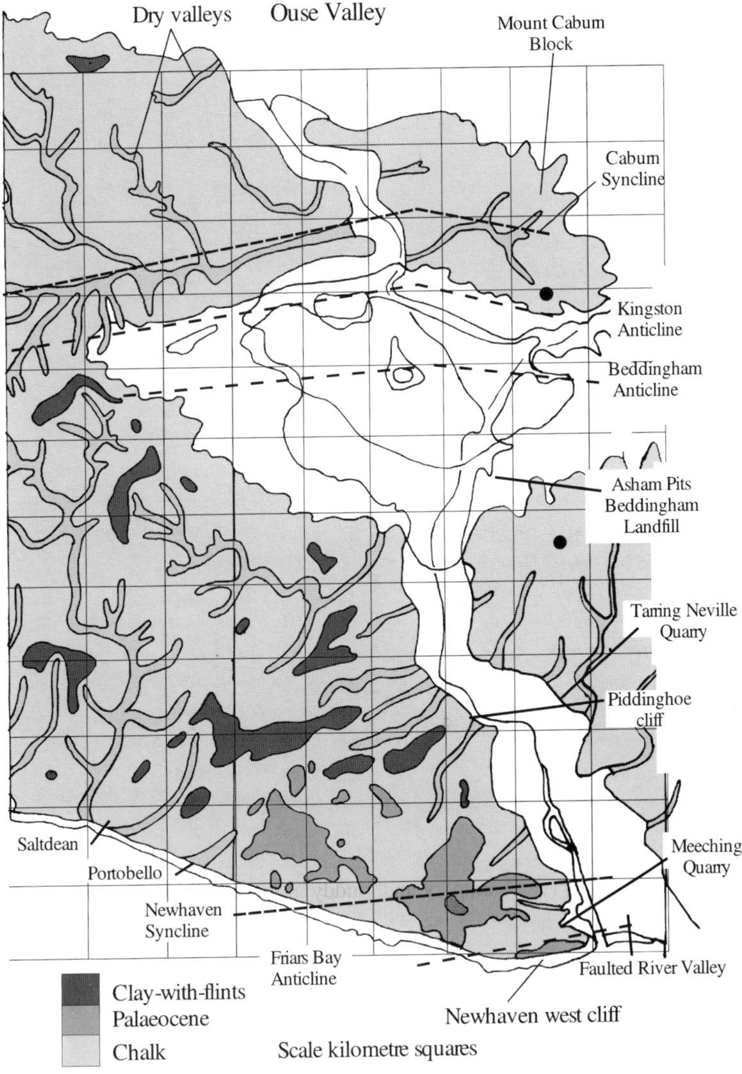

Figure 37. Geology of the Ouse Valley from Lewes to Newhaven and cliffs from Newhaven to Saltdean showing structure, drainage pattern and distribution of Palaeocene and Quaternary sediments (Clay-with-flints) on the Downs.

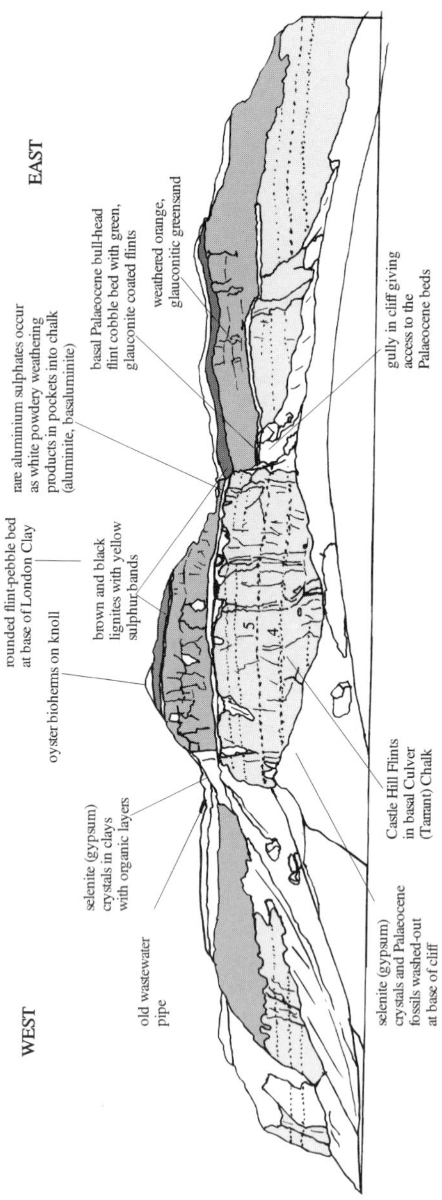

Figure 38. Castle Hill, Newhaven, showing Palaeocene deposits resting on Cretaceous (Lower Campanian Culver Chalk).

remains to be determined. Each syncline in the South Downs preserves a different age of Chalk beneath the sub-Paleocene erosion surface. At Newhaven (Newhaven Syncline) the surface cuts into Castle Hill Flints (basal G. *quadrata* Zone) while at Shoreham Harbour (Shoreham Syncline) the sub-Paleocene surface is some 30 m higher in the Culver Chalk around the level of the Charmandean Flint (mid-G. *quadrata* Zone). This illustrates the angular nature of the sub-Paleocene unconformity which cannot be fully appreciated in one exposure.

The basal Tertiary Bull-Head flint cobble bed is thicker than in many North Downs sections through it contains the same rounded and angular black and green phosphatised, glauconitised flints. This bed passes upwards into orange-weathered, green (when fresh) glauconitic, fine to medium sands with some silty and mottled clay patches, and towards the top, channel cross-bedding. A complex bed of lignites, lignitic clays with layers containing wonderful selenite crystals and yellow sulphurous bands of jarosite ($KFe_3(SO_4)_2(OH)_6$) is capped by oyster bioherms. On current Geological Survey maps these beds are known as the Woolwich facies of the Reading Formation, probably representing estuarine conditions and the lignites may have formed in abandoned channels or ox-bow lakes. This is followed by the usual basal London Clay pebble bed of rounded black or brown gravel-sized flints. The overlying blue London Clays are heavily land-slipped. Westwards, the Woolwich facies passes into more clayey deposits around Worthing but the lignites are still present beneath Shoreham Harbour where they are cemented by iron to form a deposit known locally as Stromboli. This hard material is very difficult to drill through (Mortimore, 1995c) and forms a local base for dredging Shoreham Harbour. Inland at Peacehaven, a borehole passed through the lignites into a cavity in the underlying Chalk. The Tertiary was bridging the top of the cavity. The geology map (Figure 37) shows a close spatial relationship between isolated Tertiary outcrops and surrounding patches of Clay-with-flints.

Pipes of collapsed sediments at the Chalk - Tertiary junction at Newhaven contain many rare minerals, the products of weathering processes, particularly the reaction between groundwater and pipe-fill sediments. The authigenic minerals include white cauliflower-like nodular masses of aluminite (hydrated aluminium sulphate $Al_2(SO_4)(OH)_4 *7H_20$), basaluminite. These minerals were investigated by BGS whilst remapping in the Lewes and Brighton areas (Wilmot & Young, 1985).

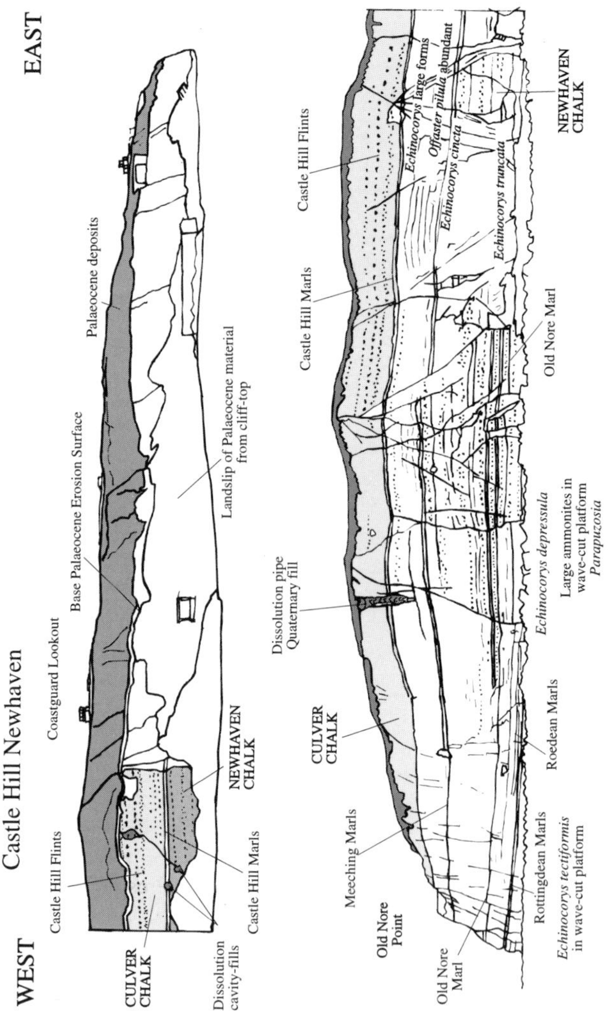

Figure 39. Sketch of Newhaven cliffs from Old Nore Point to Newhaven Harbour showing (i) continuity of flint bands and marl seams in the Newhaven and Culver Chalks, (ii) older chalk rising westwards into the cliffs on the Friar's Bay Anticline, (ii) younger chalk and thickest Palaeocene preserved in the Newhaven Syncline, (iv) dissolution pipes of different styles (and different ages?), the change from Palaeocene pipe-fills to Quaternary sediment-fills westwards. Also note dissolution of chalk along joints and the irregular sub-Palaeocene erosion surface.

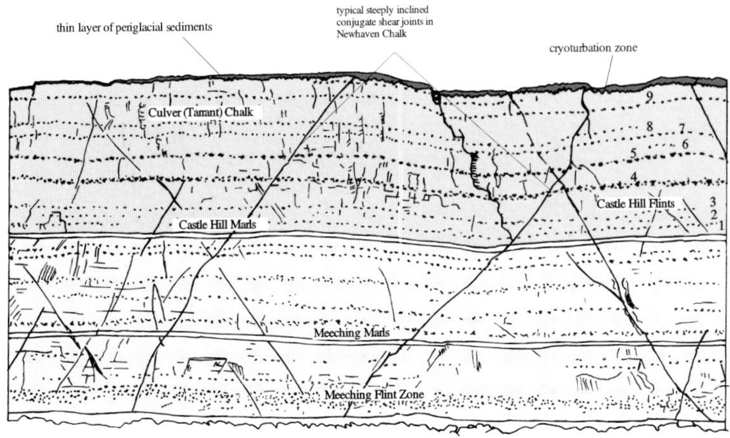

Figure 40. Sketch of the Chalk exposures in 30 m high cliffs west of Bastion Steps, Peacehaven.

Beneath the coastguard lookout on Castle Hill the Chalk contains regular bands of flint, each seam with its own character in terms of size, shape and spacing between bands and these individual band characteristics can be traced over great distances (Figures 38 to 40). Counting down from the erosive Tertiary-Chalk unconformity there are between 7-11 flint seams to the Castle Hill Marls (Figure 39) which are taken as the boundary between the Newhaven and Culver Chalks in this section (Mortimore, 1983, 1986). The Castle Hill Beds are at the base of the Culver Chalk. The pale bands between some of the flints are 'pinch and swell' small-scale layers of sliding. These bands can be traced laterally to Brighton Station where, at the same stratigraphic level, there are marl seams (Pepper Box Marls). The Castle Hill Flints contain the upper limit of the Lower Campanian *Hagenowia blackmorei* subzone (lowest subzone of the *Gonioteuthis quadrata* Zone) At this level the change from large to small forms of *Echinocorys* occurs at Castle Hill Flint number 4. *Hagenowia* is an extremely fragile, thin-shelled small echinoid (Smith & Gale, 1982) and is only rarely collected entire. Normally it is the rostra which are found in the interval between the Telscombe Marls and Castle Hill Flint Band 4 (Mortimore, 1986, fig.20).

Rarely are belemnites found, but the Arundel Sponge Bed, and the interval including Castle Hill Flints 3 and 4, have yielded *Belemnitella* and *Gonioteuthis* (Mortimore, 1986). Any further records of belemnites in this section would be invaluable.

Following the cliff westwards down the succession, each of the marker marls and flints in the Bastion Steps Beds is accessible in turn. Of interest are horizons with pseudo-laminations and intraclasts. The Telscombe Marl 1, as at Seaford Head, also contains pebble-intraclasts (intraclasts are even more abundant in this marl on the Brighton Bypass and the Arun valley). Below is the seam of scattered, mixed sized and partly tubular Tavern Flints. The three bands of large *Offaster pilula planata* (Brydone, Ernst), are between the Telscombe Marls, and the upper belt of normal sized *Offaster pilula* is below these marls and flints. The large forms of *Echinocorys* (Gaster, 1924) are also found with these flints and marls, ranging up to Castle Hill Flint Band 4 (Mortimore, 1986, fig.20).

Towards the end of the shingle beach the Meeching Marls and the belt of abundant *Echinocorys cincta* (Brydone) emerge into the cliff(Figure 39). The basal beds of the Meeching Beds are exposed in the foreshore to the east and west of the remains of an old metal groyne. The wave-washed and gullied chalk platform yields many small forms of *Echinocorys cincta* as well as several large ammonltes (*Parapuzosia? Hauericeras?*). The clean surfaces provide an excellent view of the range of trace fossils, evident by the dark grey mottling of the chalk.

Walking westwards towards Old Nore Point, the Peacehaven and Old Nore Beds are gradually exposed in turn with the marl seams forming 'flat' smooth surfaces on the wave-cut platform. Each marl forms a ledge in the cliff and the Old Nore Marl in particular is used in the spring as a nesting level for kittiwakes. This strong 10 mm thick marl seam rises into the cliff (Figure 39) on the gently dipping Friars' Bay Anticline and is a strong marker band in the cliffs westwards to Bastion Steps.

At this point it is possible to continue walking westwards to Peacehaven and Bastion Steps or return to the Newhaven car park and take vehicles via the A259 to the eastern limit of Peacehaven, where parking is possible on an unadopted road. A concrete access road leads to the top of Peacehaven steps and the cliff-top path.

Locality 2. Friar's Bay (TQ 425004).

Summary of geological interest
Newhaven Chalk Member.

Recently constructed Coastal Protection Works and the Peacehaven steps at Friar's Bay provide a section through the Newhaven Chalk. At Old Nore Point, the Brighton Marl in the *Marsupites testudinarius* Zone is exposed in the wave-cut platform. From this Point walking back and up the Steps it is possible to confirm all the key litho- and biostratigraphic levels in the Newhaven Chalk including (i) bands of *Echinocorys* with different shapes which provide ideal regional zonal? markers; (ii) *E. elevata* is in two bands between the Brighton Marl and the Friar's Bay Marl 1; (iii) *E. tectiformis* (Brydone) in and above the Friar's Bay Marls which are on either side of the horizon with *Uintacrinus anglicus* (Rasmussen); (iv) *E. depressula* (Brydone) sporadically as low as the Sheepcote valley flints in the *M. testudinarius* Zone, where it is associated with *Conulus* and *Micraster,* but it is not abundant until levels around the Rottingdean Pair of Marls; (v) *E. truncata* (Brydone) concentrated mainly in the upper belt of *Offaster pilula* (Lamarck) between the Old Nore Marl and the Peacehaven Marl

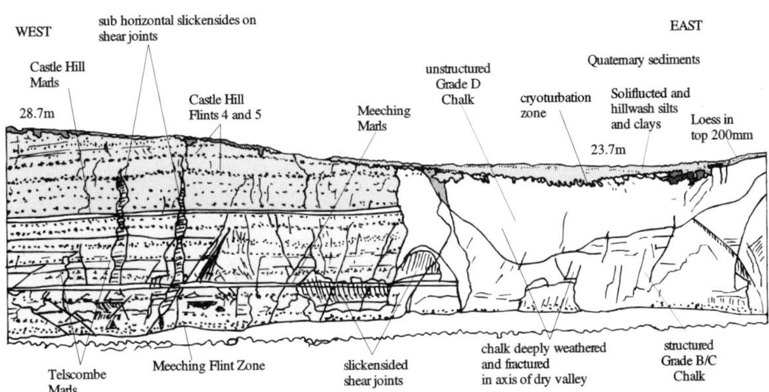

Figure 41. Sketch cross-section of typical weathering profile beneath a small chalk dry-valley west of Bastion Steps, Peacehaven cliffs. (DV1 on Map, Fig. 43).

(Peacehaven Beds); (vi) *E. cincta* (Brydone) concentrated mainly in a belt below and in the Meeching Pair of Marls, but is also found throughout the Meeching Beds; (vii) the upper belt of *O. pilula* and the overlying three bands with the larger *O. planata* (Brydone MS; Ernst) found by identifying the Tavern Flints to the Telscombe Marls. This also the level of the large forms of *Echinocorys* (Gaster, 1924); (viii) bands with the fragile small irregular echinoid *Hagenowia blackmoreii* in the higher part of the Bastion Steps and the Castle Hill Beds. The key marker marls and flints are easy to trace through the cliff face, but particularly useful for correlation are the Friar's Bay Flints, Old Nore Marl and Flints, the Meeching Marls and Castle Hill Marls and Flints. These have been proved in borehole cores and areas as far afield as Salisbury (Wiltshire) and Lulworth (Dorset) (also see Seaford Head section p.73 and Mortimore, 1987b).

Locality 3. Bastion Steps, Peacehaven (TQ 410008).

Summary of geological interest

Newhaven Chalk, Meeching and Bastion Steps Beds; Culver Chalk, Castle Hill Beds: Lower Campanian.

The same stratigraphy seen at Friar's Bay Steps is repeated at Bastion Steps, but the beds are gradually dipping west (true dip is north into the Newhaven Syncline), and as a result the Old Nore and Peacehaven Beds have passed below the base of the cliff (Figure 40). Westwards the chalk cliffs gradually truncate a dry valley system. The first of these valleys (Figure 41), illustrates the of chalk weathering beneath the valley floor. Valleys further west have cut too deeply to preserve this chalk profile.

Figure 42. Sketch of the Chalk exposed at Telscombe Cliffs in axis of Newhaven Syncline: a east side of Portobello, top Newhaven and base Culver Chalks; b. centre of bay, mixed Palaeocene and Quaternary sediments and structures resting on highly weathered Newhaven Chalk (Meeching and Bastion Steps Beds); c. west side Portobello, Old Nore Beds rise into cliff. The Portobello section cliff is weathering back as a result of both weaker, weathered chalk and the increased scour related to the outfalls and groynes.

a.

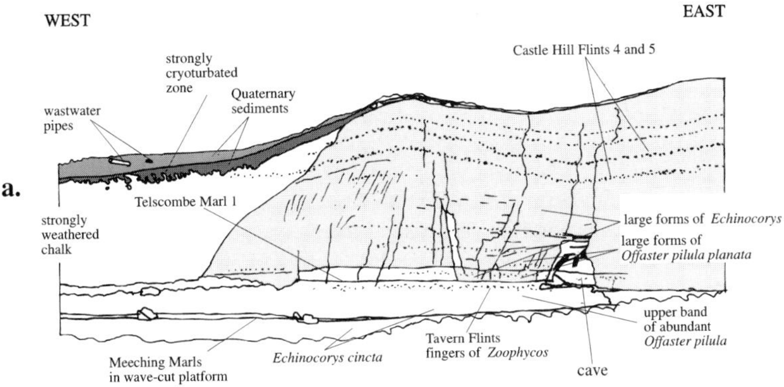
WEST
EAST
strongly
cryoturbated
zone
Quaternary
sediments
wastwater
pipes
Castle Hill Flints 4 and 5
Telscombe Marl 1
strongly
weathered
chalk
large forms of Echinocorys
large forms of
Offaster pilula planata
upper band
of abundant
Offaster pilula
Tavern Flints
fingers of Zoophycos
Meeching Marls
in wave-cut platform
Echinocorys cincta
cave

b.

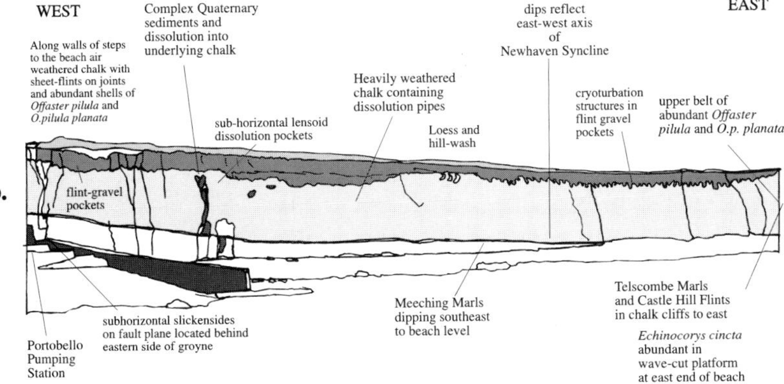
WEST
Complex Quaternary
sediments and
dissolution into
underlying chalk
dips reflect
east-west axis
of
Newhaven Syncline
EAST
Along walls of steps
to the beach air
weathered chalk with
sheet-flints on joints
and abundant shells of
Offaster pilula and
O.pilula planata
Heavily weathered
chalk containing
dissolution pipes
cryoturbation
structures in
flint gravel
pockets
upper belt of
abundant Offaster
pilula and O.p. planata
sub-horizontal lensoid
dissolution pockets
Loess and
hill-wash
flint-gravel
pockets
Telscombe Marls
and Castle Hill Flints
in chalk cliffs to east
Meeching Marls
dipping southeast
to beach level
subhorizontal slickensides
on fault plane located behind
eastern side of groyne
Portobello
Pumping
Station
Echinocorys cincta
abundant in
wave-cut platform
at east end of beach

c.

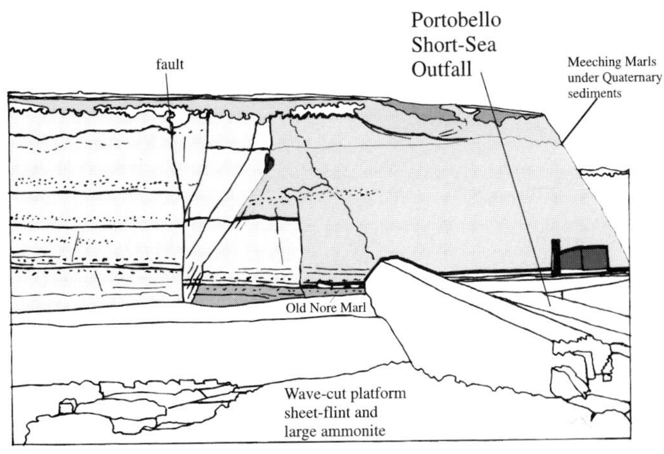
Portobello
Short-Sea
Outfall
fault
Meeching Marls
under Quaternary
sediments
Old Nore Marl
Wave-cut platform
sheet-flint and
large ammonite

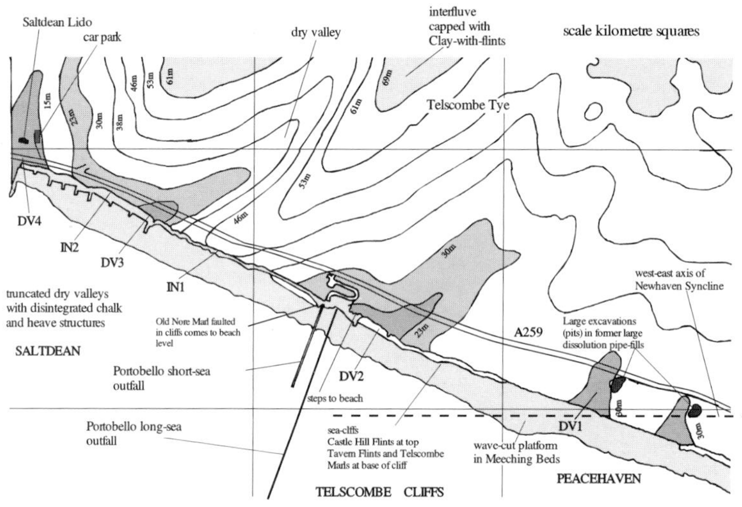

Figure 43a. Map of chalk interfluves and dry valleys around Portobello and Saltdean showing geomorphological position of truncated dry valley systems in the Newhaven Chalk. Dry valleys (DV) and interfluves(IN) are numbered from east to west. DV1=Dry valley 1 illustrated in Fig.41. DV2=Dry valley 2 at Portobello (Telscombe Cliffs) coincident with east-west axis of the Newhaven Syncline, contains heavily weathered, Liesegang-banded chalk with red-orange iron-stained joints, overlain by dissolution features and very complex Quaternary sediments. DV2 contrasts with DV3 and DV4 because it is in a syncline containing thicker Quaternary sediments (close to disturbed Palaeocene outcrop), and the presence of dissolution pipes. DV3=Dry Valley 3 with a 15 m deep exposure of weathering and heave structures (see Higginbottom, 1996) with overlying chalky and flinty Head or hill wash. Note asymmetry of valley, NW slope is steeper than SE slope. DV4=Dry Valley 4, 15 m deep exposure of weathering. IN1=Interfluve 1, 40 m high chalk cliffs with typical, steeply inclined conjugate shear joints in Newhaven Chalk. IN2=Interfluve 2, low-level toe of interfluve with disturbed and deeply weathered chalk.

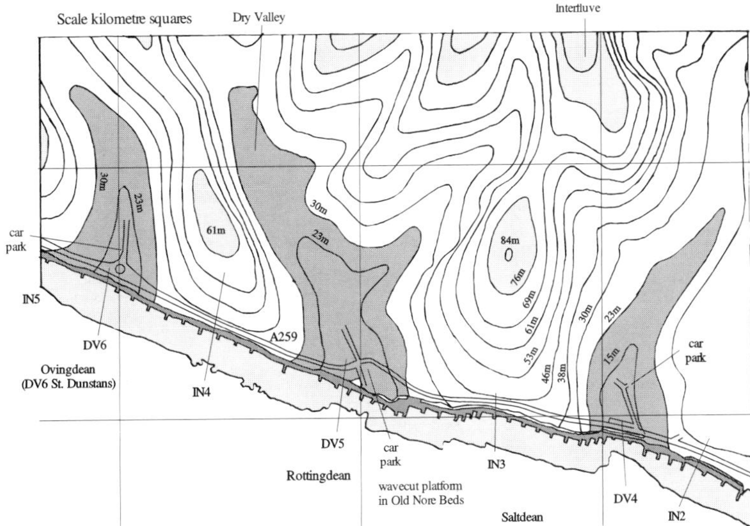

Figure 43b. Truncated dry valleys (DV) and interfluves (IN) between Saltdean and Ovingdean showing the geomorphological setting of each valley, car parking and undercliff access points. DV6 at Ovingdean (Figure 44) contains structures indicative of saturated ground conditions perhaps towards the end of the Devensian. There are sharply contrasting weathering styles between each valley and between valleys and interfluves.

Locality 4. Telscombe Cliffs (TQ 398012), **Portobello to Saltdean - Rottingdean-Ovingdean** (TQ 380018 to TQ 363023).

Summary of geological interest

Chalk weathering, Quaternary sediment-infilled solution pipes.

There are public car parks behind the Telscombe Tavern and opposite Saltdean Lido and at St Dunstan's (Figure 43).

The Peacehaven Beds gradually rise back into the cliff westwards towards Telscombe. At Portobello the Bastion Steps Beds and Culver Chalk are present on the east side of the bay (Figure 42a), and the Peacehaven Beds on the west side (Figure 42c). In the core of this bay (Figure 42b), complex Quaternary sediments are piped into the underlying chalk along dissolution features. The geology map (Figure 37) indicates that this exposure is close to the feather edge of Tertiary deposits in the Newhaven Syncline. The underlying Chalk is heavily iron-stained along joints and internally Liesegang banded. This is an excellent section for studying the weathering of the Chalk.

Between Portobello and Saltdean (Figure 43a) the cliffs are unprotected by a sea-wall, providing one of the last clean, wave-washed sections along this stretch of coast. At Saltdean the Old Nore and Peacehaven Marls and Flints form conspicuous features in the weathered and ice disturbed chalk above the sea-wall. The degree of disintegration of the chalk in the truncated valleys can be seen to be controlled by bed lithology. Harder chalk layers in the Old Nore Beds retain a more blocky structure. Marls and sheet flints act as weathering grade breaks. The impact of Quaternary cold (but humid) climatic episodes on probably fully saturated chalk has been to produce spectacular heave structures and reduction of blocky chalk to a fine silty paste (putty chalk). Experiments in France (Lautridou *et al.*, 1986), have shown that high porosity chalk is a most frost-susceptible rock and disintegrates to an optimum silty grain size during freeze-thaw cycles. Optimum climatic conditions (cold but humid) such as existed at the end of the last (Devensian) ice age 12000 years ago or during the

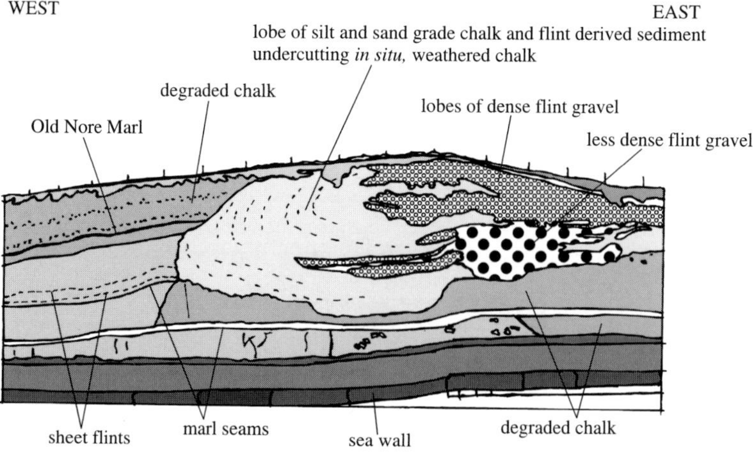

Figure 44. Weathered chalk and unusual Quaternary sedimentary structures in the floor of a Dry Valley (DV6, St. Dunstans). Lobes of sediment (filling a channel?) rest on the undercut degraded, weathered chalk. Dense flint gravels interfinger with khaki coloured silt and sand grade chalky Head (metastable, becomes mobile on wetting).

Loch Lomond Stadial (mini-Ice age about 8000 years ago) (Kerney, Brown & Chandler, 1964) would have provided ideal conditions for the development of these sediments and sedimentary structures.

At Ovingdean (Figures 43b & 44) very strange lobes of sediment have developed. These again probably reflect saturated ground conditions and relatively mobile sediments. In the coastal rock platforms from Saltdean to Rottingdean various forms of *Echinocorys* including *E. tectiformis* and *E. depressula* and a band of *Cretirhynchia* are found between the groynes.

Locality 5. Black Rock Marina (TQ 344032).

Summary of geological interest

Old Nore Beds (base of Campanian);
Black Rock Raised Beach (SSSI) deposits.

The path leading onto the undercliff walk at the eastern end of Brighton Marina allows access to the Old Nore Beds from the Rottingdean Marls down to the

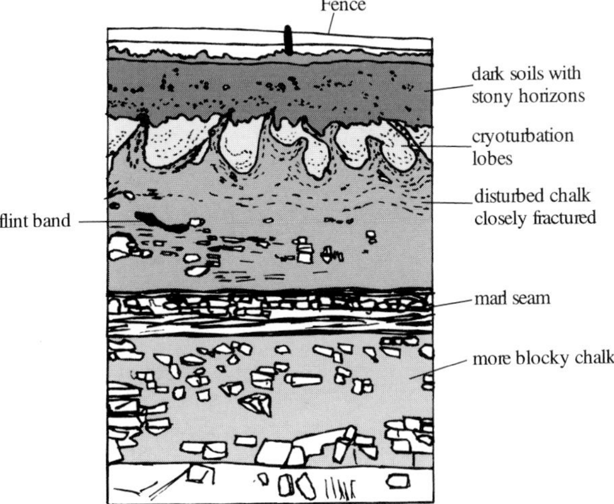

Figure 45. Quaternary structures and chalk weathering in the uppermost 3 m of cliff exposure along Black Rock access road to the undercliff walk. The Friar's Bay Marls and Flints and the uppermost occurrences of Marsupites testudinarius *are present at the junction of the track and the undercliff walk by the Marina east wall. The sketch shows the typical well-developed cryoturbation lobes present along this cliff-top and the progressive change in fracture frequency in the chalk with depth below the weathered surface.*

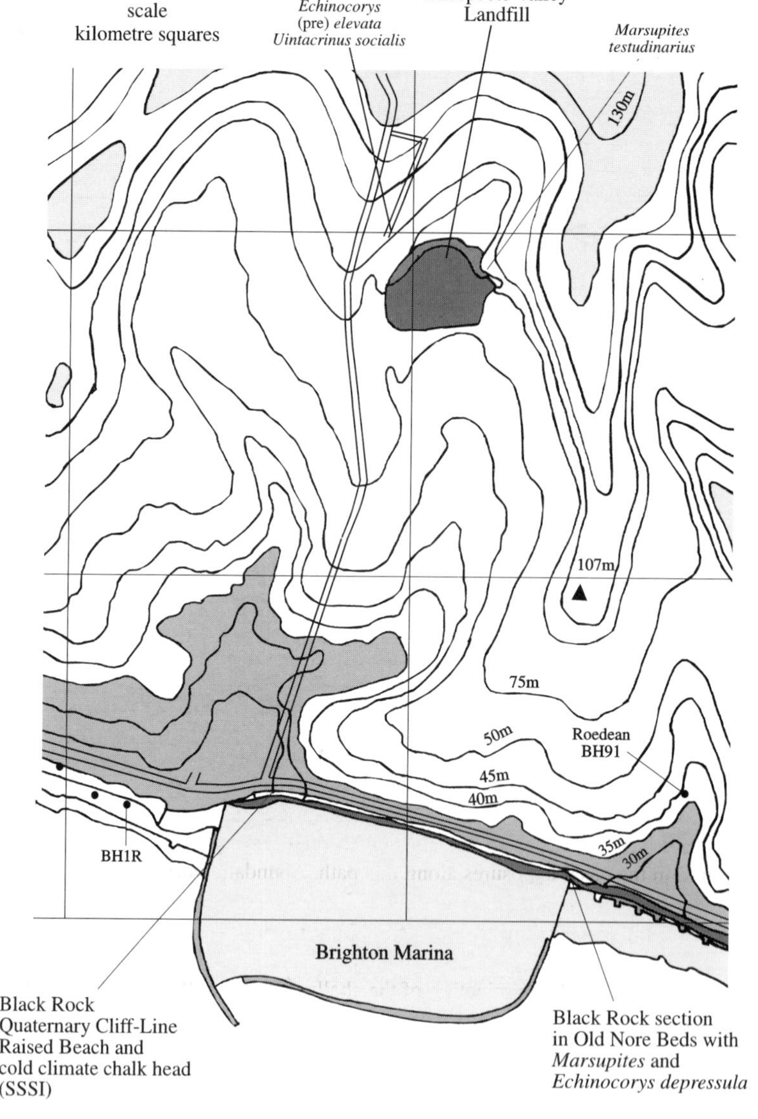

Figure 46. Map of the Black Rock area of east Brighton showing the position of the Quaternary Raised Beach (SSSI) and the exposure along the Black Rock access path of the undercliff walk.

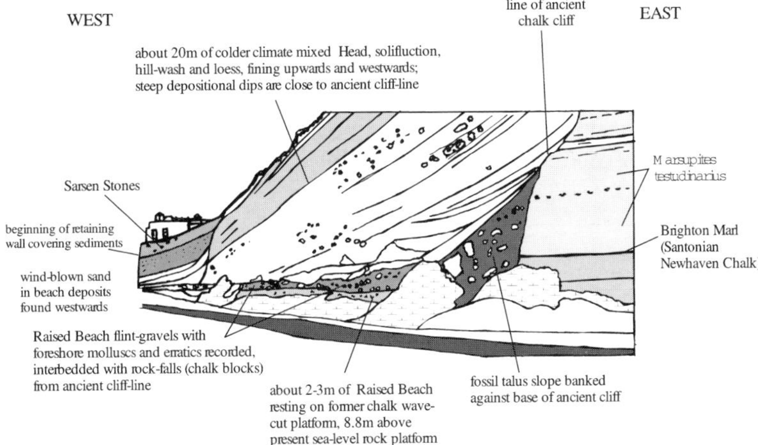

Figure 47. Black Rock, Brighton SSSI, interglacial raised beach covered by colder climate slope and Head deposits. Mammalian bones collected in the past from these deposits and similar ones at Aldrington include Elephas primigenius, Tichorhinus antiquitatis, Cervus elephus, Equus caballus, Hippopotamus amphibius *and* Sus scrofa. *The fossils cliff line, cut in Newhaven Chalk, trends inland to the NW and forms a marked break of slope through the suburbs of Brighton and Hove.*

Friar's Bay Flints and Marls. At the top of the path are cryoturbation structures (involutions, Figure 45). *Uintacrinus anglicus* and *Marsupites testudinarius* can be found in the basal exposures along this path. Abundant worn *Cretirhynchia* and beekitised fragments of inoceramids occur on the wave-cut platform adjacent to the eastern harbour wall of the Marina.

Westwards towards the termination of the chalk cliff at the Black Rock Raised Beach, the Brighton Marl and the underlying complex of five marls can be traced just above the back 'splash' wall of the undercliff sea wall (Figures 46 & 47). As the various beds of the Newhaven Chalk are traced westwards from Newhaven to Brighton there is an increase in thickness together with a better development of the marl seams. This is further emphasised at Brighton Station.

The Quaternary cliff section is an SSSI and is well worth a study (Figure 47). The influence of Quaternary climatic fluctuations has been dramatic. First there is the presumed warmer climate, higher sea-level raised beach, which is some 8 m above the present day beach nearby. Then there is the evidence for colder climates in the overlying deposits. As indicated by the work of Lautridou *et al.* (1986), great swathes of downland chalk must have been sloughed away by numerous freeze-thaw cycles in optimum, humid conditions producing the chalk head deposits that fill the dry valleys, rest on the Raised Beach and bank-up against the ancient cliff-line with steep depositional dips. It is across this cliff-line, traceable through urban Brighton by a break of slope, that many buildings have been structurally damaged by subsidence, being partly founded on Chalk and partly on Head.

The Raised Beach sediments at Black Rock pass laterally into more sandy material (no longer exposed). Further west in Sussex are other raised beach deposits at Slindon and Eartham near Chichester. These are at higher levels. Some parts of these beaches rest on Tertiary clay deposits rather than Chalk (e.g. near Slindon) and because water was trapped locally in the sands, quick sand conditions were encountered during the construction of the A27.

At the end of this excursion there are numerous cafes and pubs both in the Brighton Marina complex and in the immediately adjacent Kemptown. Bus routes run along the seafront road, A259, between Newhaven and Brighton.

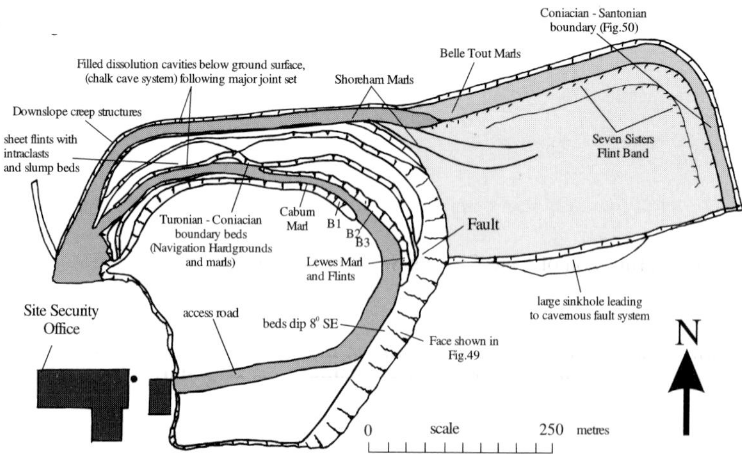

Figure 48. Sketch plan of the old Shoreham Cement Works Quarry at Upper Beeding. The position of key sections is shown. (The quarry is under review for development and the access and exposures may change in the future). B1, B2 and B3 = Bridgewick Marls.

Itinerary 5. The Adur Valley Sections.

Locality 1. Beeding Small Quarry (TQ 212101)

Summary of geological interest

Base of the Lewes Chalk; Southerham, Caburn, Bridgewick and Lewes Marls, with flint bands,

Vehicles can be parked on the wide grass verge of the A2037 Henfield Road opposite Golding Barn (TQ 208108).

The route to Beeding Small Quarry is south along the bridlepath past Golding Barn where the Plenus Marls and Melbourn Rock are present; the rock is exceptionally hard and red with iron-stained layers. The Beeding Small Pit exposes the base of the Lewes Chalk, not seen in the Cement Works Quarry to the south. Here the nodular beds are also exceptionally well developed, being rugged and hard. The Southerham, Caburn, Bridgewick and Lewes Marls are all present associated with the fossil assemblages of *Micraster, Sternotaxis* [*Holaster*], *Inoceramus* and brachiopods seen at Beachy Head and Lewes. A combination of these fossils, the marl seams and the characteristic flint bands makes detailed correlation possible. Typical of most of the South Downs, the Southerham and Caburn Flints are equally as conspicuous as the Bridgewick Flints, the latter being taken as the base of the Upper Chalk in the traditional lithostratigraphy of southern England.

Locality 2. Shoreham Cement Works, Beeding Quarry (TQ 202088).

Summary of geological interest

Lewes, Navigation, Cliffe, Beeding, Shoreham and Belle Tout Marls; Navigation Hardgrounds: Coniacian - Santonian boundary.

With the permission of Blue Circle's Security Staff at the abandoned Shoreham Cement Works it is possible to park a car at the top of the concrete road leading to the upper entrance to the main pit or park in the bottom of the pit near the security office (Figure 48). (**The signing of indemnity forms, the wearing of helmets and the following of safety procedures are essential**). From the vantage point looking into the pit from the northwest end, a general picture of the stratigraphy can be established (Figure 49):-
(i) the lowest beds exposed (in 1977) were in the lower Lewes Chalk between the Southerham and Caburns Marls (*Terebratulina lata* Zone), backfilling has now covered most of the Caburn and Ringmer Beds;
(ii) marker marl seams form distinct ledges around the quarry walls, particularly the Lewes, Navigation, Cliffe, Beeding and Shoreham Marls;
(iii) the dominant feature of the quarry is the rock band formed by the three

Navigation Hardgrounds which have welded together (Figures 48 & 49);
(iv) above the Shoreham Marls - Belle Tout Marls is the conspicuous Seven Sisters Flint Band;
(v) recent (1980-87) excavation in the upper eastern part of the quarry has exposed the Cuckmere and basal Haven Brow Beds in the *M. coranguinum* Zone at the Coniacian-Santonian boundary.

Other features of the geology are (i) the similarity of the rock fracture patterns compared with Seaford Head; (ii) a conspicuous fault on the eastern wall, downthrowing 4 m to the southeast, expanded into cavities by solution, which in wet winters carried vast quantities of water that flooded the floor of the quarry: air photographs show that the eastward extension of this fault is marked by a line of depressions (swallow holes?) at the downland surface one of which has been cut through by the quarrying (Figure 48); (iii) exploitation of faults and the main inclined shear planes by periglacial and solution processes, resulting in considerable quantities and varieties of sediments (sands, red clays, Clay-with-flints and silts penetrating to considerable depths into the chalk; (iv) over-fold structures indicating down-slope creep and development of gulls towards the Adur Valley.

The lowest sections in Beeding Quarry.
Descend the roadway leading to the floor of the quarry, where the rough nodular layers typical of the Lewes Chalk and the nodular, horn-flint seams with their distinctive grey texture are a feature of this level. Interbedded with the nodular chalk are 'wavy' and interlaced marl seams (griotte or flaser texture). Fossils are not abundant but examples of *Sternotaxis plana* and pleurotomariid gastropods can be obtained.

The lowest of the key marker marls exposed is the Caburn Marl, the top surface of which is taken as the boundary between the Caburn and overlying Ringmer Beds. The more accessible Bridgewick Marls (70-200 mm thick), in particular the Bridgewick Marl 1, provide excellent examples of the sedimentary structure of marl seams. 'Augen' of chalk tend to concentrate at the bottom and top of the marl, but on breaking these augen parallel to bedding, they are shown to be the deformed chalk-fills of branching *Thalassinoides* and other burrows. In the more indurated chalk below the marl the continuations of the burrows are less deformed and, therefore, circular in cross-section, without many of the 'wispy' horsetails of marl present in the deformed layers. Small, fragile, spiny spondylids, oysters and inoceramids are usually quite abundant in the marl which also contains abundant *Terebratulina lata* (a 'dwarf' fauna?). These marls are also distinctly green in colour. Several *Micraster corbovis* of *lata* Zone type (Rowe, 1899; *Roweaster rowei* Drummond ms) have been collected here below the Bridgewick Marl 1.

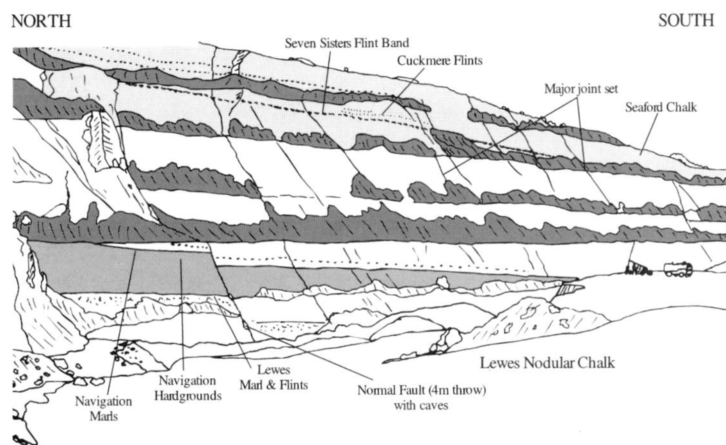

Figure 49. Shoreham Cement Works, Upper Beeding Quarry, sketch of the main face looking east. Lewes Nodular Chalk occupies most of the exposure with Seaford Chalk present in the uppermost sections.

From the upper Kingston Beds a variety of fossils have been collected including *Allocrioceras,* scaphitids, trochids, pleurotomarids, *Cretirhynchia minor* (Pettitt), *Cretirhynchia cuneiformis* (Pettitt), *Cretirhynchia octoplicata* (Sowerby), *Orbirhynchia reedensis* (Etheridge) and the small variety of *Micraster leskei* (Desmoulins), all indicative of a level equating with the top of the 'Chalk Rock', but in Sussex without the chalk rock lithology. Current research is investigating the exact relationship of individual beds in the condensed Chalk Rock to the expanded sequences of Sussex.

There is also an excellent view of the remarkable Lewes Flints, layers of 'tubular or finger-flints' extending down through some 3 m of nodular chalks below the Lewes Marl. Similar, but squatter, more dumbell-shaped flints occur above the Lewes Marl.

There is an abundance of the characteristic large *Micraster leskei* occurring in and above the Lewes Marl, followed by the griotte-nodular chalks up to the Lewes Nodular Chalks containing *Micraster precursor* (pars sensu Rowe, Drummond, 1983). *Lewesiceras* of a special form has also been collected in beds immediately above the Lewes Marls. These beds are then succeeded by a soft chalk unit within which the trace fossil *Zoophycos* is abundant (the Cuilfail Zoophycos). Large, fragile *Sternotaxis placenta* (Agassiz) and *Micraster normanniae* (Bucaille) occur here in these softer chalks and from the overlying massively bedded and strongly nodular Navigation Hardgrounds. These hardgrounds form a spectacular rock band, comprising several nodular layers welded together. The lowest bed has a glauconite-coated, convolute upper surface and the whole complex forms a rugged unit around the lower part of the quarry. The thickness of chalk between the Lewes and Navigation Marls at Shoreham is half that of the Lewes area. Within these hardgrounds, inoceramids indicative of the Turonian - Coniacian boundary, are present (e.g. *Inoceramus lusatiae*).

Above the Navigation Hardgrounds, are the two Navigation Marls, similar to the pair of marls at Seaford Head, but here only 0.2-0.3m apart although retaining the typical carious flints between them. Within the Cliffe and Hope Gap Beds above are two marl seams containing shattered and fragmented flint shards and with other lithoclastic debris. These are at levels comparable with those at Hope Gap (p.60). The same layers had also been found in the Arun valley, at Houghton quarries, indicating a widespread stratigraphic level of 'disturbance' within the South Downs.

The Cliffe, Hope Gap and Beeding Flints are also well developed here. Many of the fossils are Liesegang-banded where found close to the major fractures with karst features.

The Turonian - Coniacian boundary problem.

Late Turonian *Mytiloides* have been found in beds up to the base of the Cuilfail Zoophycos horizon and possibly to the base of the Navigation Hardgrounds. A band of *Cremnoceramus rotundatus* has been identified 0.7 m above the upper Navigation Marl and abundant *Cremnoceramus? waltersdorfensis* is present in the overlying 3 m. The interval represented by the Navigation Beds is, therefore, of uncertain age but microfossil evidence (Pomerol *et al.*, 1987) suggests that most of it is Coniacian. Thus the basal limits of the range of *Micraster normanniae* ss would represent the basal Zone of the Coniacian in chalk facies. No diagnostic ammonites have been found at this level and any records would be of great stratigraphic value. In addition, the ammonite *Subprionocyclus* is unrecorded in these Sussex sections between the Lewes and Navigation Marls.

The upper sections in Beeding Quarry: Beeding Beds to Belle Tout Beds: Lewes Chalk - Seaford Chalk junction: mid- and high Coniacian.

The remainder of the quarry succession is most easily examined by following the access roadway closest to the northern face shaded roadway, (Figure 48).

In the succeeding beds up to the top of the Lewes Chalk the persistence of individual layers of red, iron-stained nodular horizons and conspicuous flint seams can be seen. On the banks immediately south of this road the Beeding Hardgrounds are particularly evident and contain abundant cidarids and *Micraster decipiens* (Bayle). Multicoloured bands staining the chalk parallel to the fractures, a result of several solution features following shear planes, are a guide to these beds here. Many of the *Micraster* from the adjacent Beeding Beds are similarly stained.

At the top of the Lewes Chalk are the extremely well developed Shoreham Marls and the detailed similarities of the Shoreham Beds with Seaford Head can be seen, even to the individual character of the flints and the grey-white alternations of the chalk beds. In addition, the marked change in gross lithology from the Lewes to the Seaford Chalk is easy to distinguish, both as a result of the purer and more homogeneous nature of the Seaford Chalk and of the resulting more uniform fracturing into smaller blocks. There is thus a unity to the major lithological divisions recognised in the Sussex Chalk, as well as a reliable marker bed stratigraphy.

The Seven Sisters Flint is the major marker layer across the quarry faces, dipping southeast at about 8°. Between the Shoreham Marls and this marker flint is an exceptionally marly sequence in which the Belle Tout Marls are the most prominent. These are again associated with layers of abundant bivalve debris, *Platyceramus* and volviceramids (see also Birling Gap and Seaford Head above). *Volviceramus* ex gr. *involutus* (J. de C. Sowerby) is particularly abundant in a band 1.6-1.7 m below the Seven Sisters Flint. *Micraster turonensis* and depressed forms of *Echinocorys* are the most common echinoids. Plant debris is particularly common on some of the Belle Tout marly surfaces and the Belle Tout Beds are more marly than on the coast.

Extensive carious dissolution of a fault plane and cementation of the surrounding chalk can be seen in the far northeast corner of the quarry. This relates well to a the former position of a swallow-hole which is evident on old aerial photographs taken before this part of the quarry was excavated. The fault seen at the base of the pit is a continuation of part of this same fault complex.

Seaford Chalk, Cuckmere Beds: Bedwell's Columnar Flint: Coniacian - Santonian boundary.

The Belle Tout and Cuckmere Beds are thicker here and contain more marl seams than on the coast sections. The flints are also correspondingly better developed. A very fine section is accessible through the Cuckmere beds to the three flint bands associated with the basal Santonian (Figure 50). *Micraster coranguinum* (Leske) and *Micraster* related to *M. bucaillei* are fairly common but the inoceramid bivalve debris disappears at the upper Cuckmere

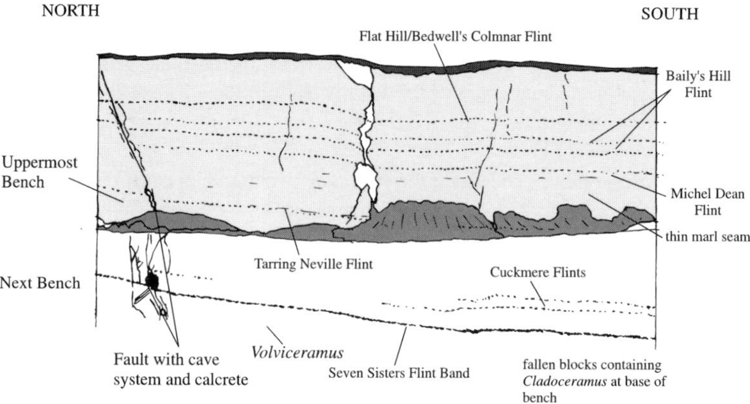

Figure 50. Shoreham Cement Works, Upper Beeding Quarry, uppermost exposure, far eastern face, showing the key marker flints in the Seaford Chalk.

Flint. Superb examples of *Cladoceramus undulatoplicatus* and barrel-shaped *Bourgueticrinus* can be collected from the uppermost beds of the pit.

The view from this high point in the quarry over the Adur Valley towards Lancing College looks onto Lancing Hill and Steep Down which are the beginnings of the Secondary Escarpment, related to the thicker development of Newhaven Chalk. The lower flatter ground to the north on the main escarpment dipslope is formed in Seaford Chalk.

KENT CHALK ITINERARIES

Kentish Chalk is famous for the White Cliffs of Dover and these cliffs are the natural starting point for six itineraries studying the Chalk of the north rim of the Weald. Despite the long history of interest in the White Cliffs Chalk it is only relatively recently that detailed correlations have been made between Langdon Bay, East Cliff, Dover and Aker's Steps, Shakespeare Cliff and Aycliff using for example the Southerham and Caburn Marl seams. The West Melbury Marly Chalk (Chalk Marl) as the main tunnelling horizon for the Channel Tunnel has been studied in immense detail and individual marl and limestone beds have been correlated (Destombes & Shephard-Thorn, 1971; Gale, 1989a,b; 1995; Harris *et al.,* 1996).

An account of the Channel Tunnel construction is given in *Proceedings of the Institution of Civil Engineers* (Special issue, 1992). More detail on the geology of the Channel Tunnel and Dover-Folkestone works is given in *Engineering Geology of the The Channel Tunnel* (1996, Thomas Telford publishers). Folkestone Warren landslips are famous for disruption of the Folkestone - Dover Railway (Osman, 1917; Wood, 1955; Toms, 1966,; Hutchinson, 1968, 1969).

Detailed studies of the North Downs Chalk (Robinson, 1986) introduced a parallel stratigraphy to that of the South Downs. A unified stratigraphy for the Chalk of the Weald has been introduced for British Geological Survey mapping (Bristow *et al.,* In prep.) and it is this nomenclature that is used here. Nevertheless, the field section details of Robinson (1986) are a very useful reference. Price (1874, 1877) introduced bed numbers for the Gault which are still widely used and identified horizons such as the 'Cast Bed' in the Lower Chalk, a key marker horizon. Carter and Hart (1977) introduced a microfossil zonation for the Gault - Lower Chalk with bed numbers which have been widely used during work on the Channel Tunnel (Hart, 1995). Kennedy's (1969) account of the Lower Chalk is still used as a key reference for biostratigraphy modified by information given in GA field meeting Reports (Wood, 1963; Gale, 1989) and Gale (1990, 1995).
Of the many studies of the white Upper Chalk those of Whitaker (1865, 1872), Dowker (1870), and Bedwell (1874) are the most significant in terms of marker bed identification e.g. Bedwell's Columnar Flint and Whitaker's Three Inch Flint in the Dover and Isle of Thanet sections. Rowe's (1900) study of the biostratigraphy is still used as a major reference.

In each excursion only the most conspicuous, key marker beds or fossils are described so that users of the guide can interpret the stratigraphy and understand the concepts involved. More detail is available in the references given.

Itinerary 6. Folkestone. The Warren to Abbot's Cliff, Lydden Spout, Akers Steps and Aycliff.

A good meeting point is East Cliff Pavilion, Folkestone (TR 39364, Figure 51), where cars can be parked easily at the Pavilion and on Wear Bay Road. There are two main routes through the Warren geology. The first is to follow the beach from Copt Point to the sea defences and then to Abbots Cliff. The second route is through the landslips on the tracks at the northeastern end of the car park by Martello Tower 2 (if the barrier is open cars can be taken down the tracks towards the sea defences but, sadly, cars are broken into here; it is safer to leave cars at the car park).

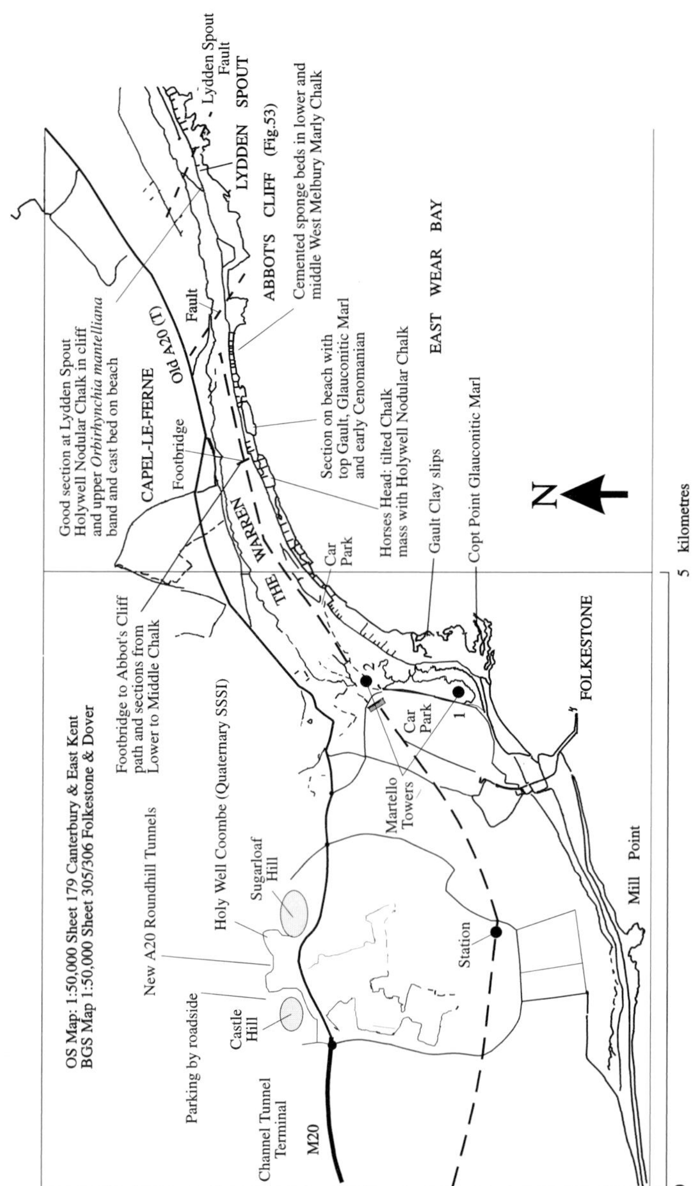

Figure 51. Localities for Itinerary 6 in the Folkestone Warren and Castle Hill areas, Kent.

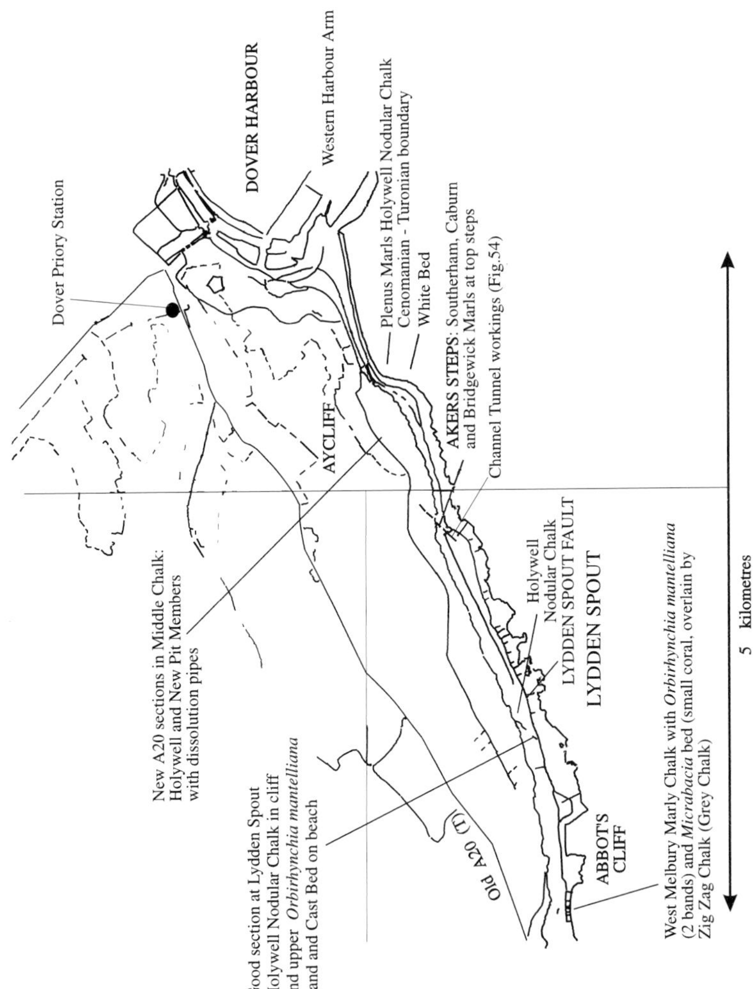

Figure 52. The traverse from Folkestone to Dover via the Warren, Abbot's Cliff, Shakespeare Cliff and Aycliff (continuation of Figure 51).

Locality 1. Copt Point (TR 243364)

Summary of geological interest

Gault, Glauconitic Marl, landslipped Chalk.

Walk towards Copt Point where the base of the Lower Chalk is usually visible, though sometimes it may be covered by landslips. The basal unit is the Glauconitic Marl (called by the French term Tourtia in the Channel Tunnel workings (Destombes & Shephard-Thorn, 1971). The Glauconitic Marl and the underlying top of the Gault (Bed 6a, Hart, 1995) are very variable in thickness. As at Cow Gap, Eastbourne, the Glauconitic Marl comprises phosphatic fragments in a silty matrix of dark green glauconite and fossil debris.

Walk northeast from Copt Point past the landslipped Gault Clay (TR 244368) and below Folkestone Warren towards Abbots Cliff. The Gault is described in detail in the companion Guide to the Weald (Ruffell *et al.,* 1996).

Along the backcliff to the undercliff sea wall (TR 244372) dislodged masses of various levels in the Chalk are present, particularly the ‘gritty’ Melbourn Rock - Holywell Nodular Chalk and the underlying White Bed (the unit about 14 m thick at the top of the Zig Zag Chalk Member). Two landslipped pinnacles of steeply dipping Holywell Nodular Chalk are conspicuous features on the sea-wall walk to Abbot’s Cliff. One of these slipped blocks is known as the Horses Head (Figure 53), and contains *Mytiloides,* ossicles of starfish, small echinoids and brachiopods, particularly *Orbirhynchia cuvieri.* The sea wall, designed to provide toe-weight against further landslip, is disintegrating and these sections may change drastically during the lifetime of this guide.

Locality 2. Railway footbridge (TR 259383).

Summary of geological interest

Viewpoint: sedimentary structures.

At the eastern end of the Warren, a footbridge over the Folkestone-Dover railway (Figure 51) provides a general vantage point for the cliff opposite (to the north) with its fine examples of the chalk stratigraphy of the area. The conspicuous alternations of dark marl and pale limestone occur towards the base of the exposure. Bed 7 of Jukes-Browne and Hill ((1903), hard grey with stony lumps), is identified by the rougher weathering surfaces interpreted as scratch markings by Kennedy (1969). Others have thought these might be gutter casts (infilled grooves) caused by storms (it is easier to study these same structures in fresh exposures at Beachy Head, but their presence here indicates their wide lateral extent).

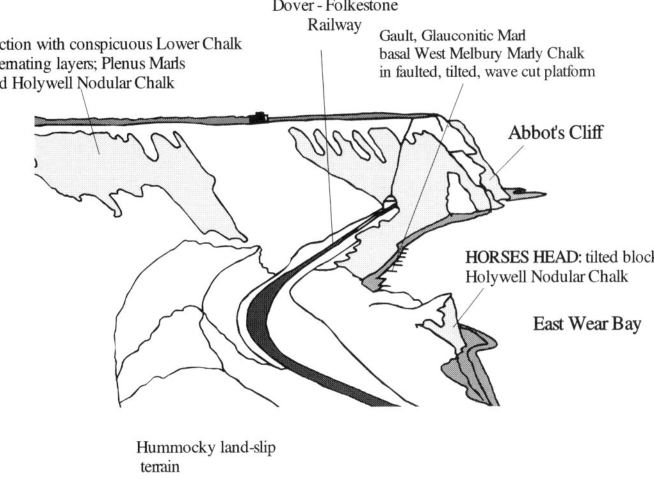

Figure 53. Sketch looking east across Folkestone Warren to Abbot's Cliff showing the position of key sections.

The Plenus Marls and gritty Holywell Nodular Chalk stand out in the cliff above separated from JB Bed 7 by JB Bed 8, the White Bed. A fine photograph of this section showing these alternations and lithostratigraphic units is given in Gale (1995, fig. 7, top photograph). The alternating beds are inferred to have been climatically controlled (Gale, 1995). The resulting cyclostratigraphy is used for correlation.

Locality 3. Eastern end of concrete platform (TR 263384).

Summary of geological interest
Plenus Marls.

Before scrambling down to the beach across rock falls at the eastern end of the concrete platform it is worth identifying the air-weathered section in the Plenus Marls. The details of Jefferies (1963), 8 bed divisions of the Plenus Marls, are more easily seen here than at Aycliff (see below). An immensely detailed account of the microfossils and geochemistry of this section has been undertaken

(Jarvis *et al,* 1988, but see comments on the Beachy Head section). This is one horizon where belemnites can be found regularly *(Actinocamax plenus)* and this fossil identifies Jefferies Bed 4.

Locality 4. Beach below Abbot's Cliff (TR 271385)

Summary of geological interest
Cenomanian Lower Chalk

Recent cliff falls (1987-88) have made access to the beach below Abbot's Cliff difficult at high tide; **a falling tide is safer.** Having negotiated these falls there is a rewarding section in the upper part of the West Melbury Marly Chalk and the Zig Zag Chalk towards Lydden Spout (TR 282387). By scrambling along and up the grassy slopes most of the Lower Chalk stratigraphy can be studied.

The main features of this cliff section are shown on the log (Figure 54). It is useful to identity individual beds with a particular group of fossils or groups of beds. For example:
(i) a group of four poorly developed limestones overlain by a prominent limestone in the basal two metres of cliff east of Abbot's Cliff. This is the middle unit in which *Orbirhynchia mantelliana* is abundant;
(ii) the conspicuous limestone is one of three, each approximately 200-300 mm thick and separated by 450-550 mm of dark marl. The succeeding 1 m contains abundant, diverse brachiopods notably *Modestella geinitzi*, and occasional small corals, *Micrabacia coronula* (Goldfuss) and this is the Cast Bed of Price (1877). The Cast Bed is so-called because of the moulds of gastropods collected there in the last century. The underlying limestone is taken as the boundary between the West Melbury Marly Chalk and the Zig Zag Chalk Members;
(iii) two thin (15-200 mm thick) limestone ribs above which is a broad, 1.5 m thick band of marly chalk containing the uppermost band of *Orbirhynchia mantelliana* (this is the *O. mantelliana* **Band 10** of Kennedy, 1969);
(iv) a succession of 9 more or less equally developed, 120-200 mm thick, conspicuous limestone bands. The lowermost two limestones are discontinuous concentrations of sponges. On the upper surface of number 8 the small coral *Micrabacia coronula* is again abundant (this is the *Micrabacia* **Band 11** of Kennedy, 1969). The relatively large brachiopod *Concinnithyris subundata* is also abundant throughout this interval and above the *Micrabacia* band.

Ammonites are the zonal and subzonal indices in the Cenomanian Lower Chalk and are present in the Abbot's Cliff sections. Brachiopods are useful for correlation because the levels of abundance are often recovered in borehole cores whereas the ammonites are rare in core. Large *Acanthoceras* of the Middle

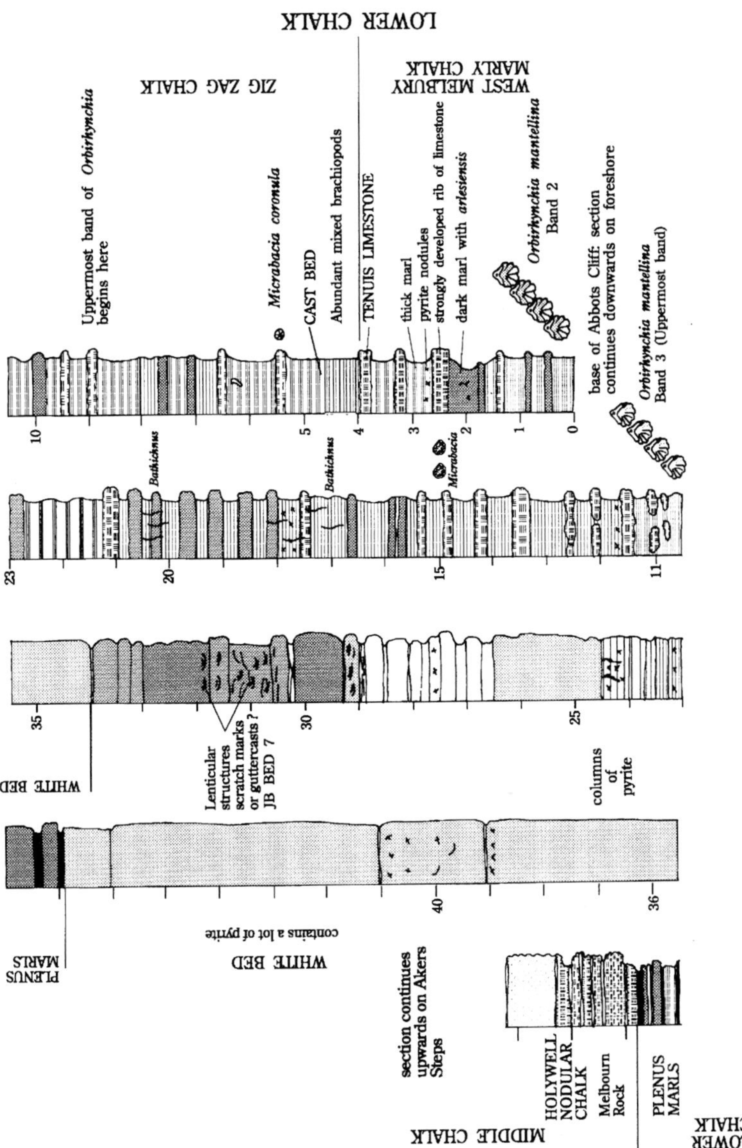

Figure 54. Geological section through the Lower Chalk exposed in Abbot's Cliff, Folkestone. The section continues below on the foreshore in faulted and tilted blocks (see Gale, 1988).

Cenomanian are occasionally found with the first interval described above containing *Orbirhynchia mantelliana*. Below this marker interval are Lower Cenomanian beds containing *Mantelliceras*.

If detailed section logging is undertaken then the consistency and utility of individual beds of chalk can be discovered when comparisons and correlations are made with the Sussex sections at Southerham, Lewes and Beachy Head. Inconsistencies arise where beds thin and/or disappear laterally over tectonically controlled synsedimentary axes as is the case in the traverse of boreholes across the Channel (Harris *et al.,* 1996). Even in these situations it is possible to recognise one or two key marker horizons which continue while intervening chalks disappear.

The dip brings each of the beds described above to beach level eastwards towards Lydden Spout. Because of rockfalls the exposure changes from year to year and not all beds will be seen in one visit.

Locality 5. East Wear Bay wave cut platform (TR 261383).

Summary of geological interest

Top Gault, Glauconitic Marl and basal West Melbury Marly Chalk: Albian - Cenomanian boundary and Lower Cenomanian biostratigraphy.

At the base of the cliffs on the faulted wave-cut platform at the eastern end of the groynes in East Wear Bay (TR 261383) it is usually possible to study lower beds in the West Melbury Marly Chalk only at low tide. The sections are often covered by weed and algae and are best studied after storms. These exposures, described by Gale (1989, locality 3), take the Lower Chalk stratigraphy below levels exposed at Southerham. Brain sponges (so-called because of their convoluted structure) are a feature of the limestone bands. Lower Cenomanian ammonites, *Mantelliceras* and *Mariella*, are relatively common. The best sections here are often covered by cliff falls. Of particular interest in comparison to the Sussex sections at Southerham Grey Pit, Lewes, is the absence at Abbot's Cliff of the *M. saxbii* event bed (Figure 7) due to post-sedimentary erosion (considered by some to be a sequence boundary). However, the 'rib' (M5 of Gale, 1989) and 'bank' of limestones so prominent at Southerham can also be identified at Abbot's Cliff. M6 (Gale, 1989) is the pair of limestones at the top of the 'bank' at Southerham. The base of the *dixoni* Zone is marked by a very dark marl (M4 of Gale, 1989) with phosphates, which is burrowed down into the underlying pale coloured limestone (M3 of Gale, 1989) which contains abundant three-dimensional *Schloenbachia*. The underlying beds comprise strongly developed marl - limestone couplets with *Sharpeiceras*, common *Rastellum colubrinum* (very strong zig-zag edged oyster) and the brachiopod *Tropeothyris carteri*. The importance of this section is that the earliest Cenomanian is developed as marl - limestone couplets, whereas at Eastbourne (Cow Gap) this same succession of couplets is incorporated in the upper part of the Glauconitic Marl. At Southerham Grey Pit these lowest beds are not exposed but are present having been seen in core. This Abbot's Cliff section is the only place where *Sharpeiceras* beds can be studied. At Craelius 1 Borehole (Aycliff) the Glauconitic Marl is very thin (0.4 m) whereas at the Abbots Cliff section the Glauconitic Marl is very thick (7 m). Sadly, these beds are often covered by rock-falls but, when exposed at low tide, tend to get 'Cenomaniacs' very excited.

Price's (1874) bed numbering for the Gault is used by most workers and it is Beds XII and XIII that are exposed here at low tide. Bed XII (about 1m thick) is terminated by an omission surface with dark clayey and phosphatic base of Bed XIII resting on it. According to Gale (1989) both Bed XIII and the overlying Glauconitic Marl are each 7 m thick followed by the basal beds of the West Melbury Marly Chalk. Gale (1989) has recorded the basal Lower Cenomanian index ammonites (see Gale's Field Meeting Report for details).

If the return walk is through the tracks of the Warren the position of Beaumont's pioneering tunnel (a forerunner of the Channel Tunnel) is passed close to Martello Tower adjacent to the barrier and the car park (Figure 51). The Whitaker's tunnelling machine, only recently recovered from these trial borings, was on display at the Eurotunnel Centre.

Locality 6. Lydden Spout (TR 283387).

Summary of geological interest

Holywell Nodular Chalk.

For those keen on walking it is possible to follow the cliff top path (North Downs Way) from Folkestone to Aycliff, Dover. En route, the steep tracks down the cliffs at Lydden Spout and Aker's Steps can be negotiated, but these tracks are for the experienced and sure-footed only.

Lydden Spout track sections expose the Holywell Nodular Chalk in spectacular air-weathered sections, with the shelly debris of *Mytiloides* the most obvious feature. There are also wonderful small echinoids and brachiopods standing out in these faces. The Dover sections are much more condensed than at Beachy Head and Lewes at this level so the Meads Marls and individual Holywell Marls are difficult or impossible to identity. Huge open fissures are visible in the cliff top. These are apparently not related to cliff movements but to construction of the railway tunnels between Folkestone and Dover.

Locality 7. Akers Steps (TR 297393).

Summary of geological interest

Bridgewick Flints and Bridgewick Marls, Caburn, Southerham and Glynde Marls, Holywell Nodular Chalk and Plenus Marls.

This is a dangerous section to visit. Akers Steps (Figure 55) provided a unique linking section to the East Cliff at Dover where the lowest beds at the base of Langdon Stairs reappear at the top of Akers Steps. This section became disused and inaccessible during construction of the Channel Tunnel. Nevertheless, it is still accessible with care and is a very important section for the Dover and North Downs Chalk. The path zig-zags steeply down the cliff, partly in an artificial gully and overlooks the Channel Tunnel Shakespeare Cliff construction site. At the top of the cliff the large Bridgewick Flints and the Bridgewick Marl Seams can seen. These are followed sequentially downwards by the Caburn Marl and underlying flints, the Southerham Marls and Flints and then the last flint above the Glynde Marls. Following the track down the entry of the Holywell Nodular

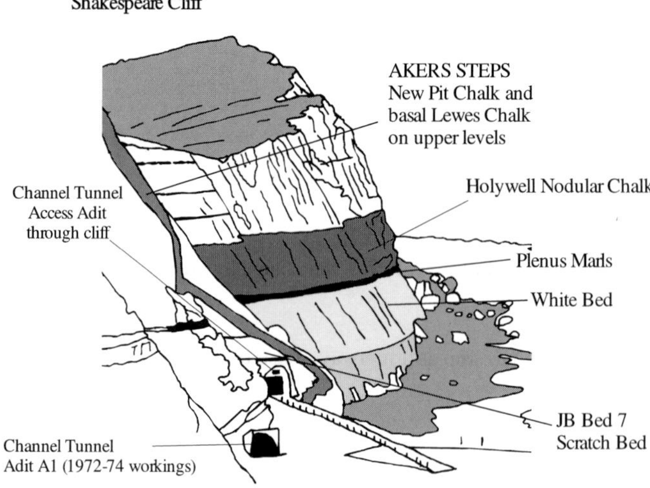

Figure 55. Looking east from the cliff top North Downs Way near Lydden Spout, across Akers Steps to Shakespeare Cliff.

Chalk is conspicuous with hard, gritty shelly, nodular chalks. The Plenus Marls below are usually covered by undergrowth. Over the top of the railway tunnel portal, but inaccessible, is the JB Bed 7, or scratch bed (Kennedy, 1969) with the scratch marks standing proud on the air-weathered exposure.

Locality 8. Aycliff (TR 308399).

Summary of geological interest

White Bed, Plenus Marls and Holywell Nodular Chalk.

Construction of the new A20 between Folkestone and Dover through Aycliff has altered the arrangements for parking but the cliff top path is still accessible as before. Vehicles can be parked in Aycliff to the north of the A20 but the Aycliff road needs to be followed out of Dover. A footbridge leads over the A20 onto the cliff top path. Uphill to the west leads to Akers Steps with fine views along the coastal cliffs. Downhill eastwards leads to the footbridge over the railway to the beach. West of the beach steps the chalk cliff exposes the White Bed, Plenus Marls and the Holywell Nodular Chalk. Each of these units is very different and condensed compared with the East Sussex sections. Yet these sections have been used to determine the macro-, microfossil and geochemical character of the Cenomanian - Turonian (C/T) boundary (Jeans *et al.,* 1991; Jarvis *et al,* 1988; Lamolda *et al.,* 1994) (see discussion in Wood & Mortimore, 1995).

The Folkestone to Aycliff sections can be completed in one day but the Warren - Abbots Cliff alone can take a whole day. There are several excellent picnic stops. Castle Hill on the Pilgrims Way (TR 13380) offers a sheltered spot overlooking the Channel Tunnel terminals, the A20 Round Hill Tunnels and Folkestone. From this vantage point, those interested in geomorphology can study the change of slope on Sugarloaf Hill opposite where an ancient Quaternary slip had to be stabilised as part of the tunnel construction. To prevent further slips along the escarpment vast volumes of gravel from the channel were pumped ashore and spread along the toe of the scarp slope.

There is also a good pub stop as a halfway house between Folkestone and Aycliff on the crest of the escarpment along the old Dover-Folkestone Road (TR 241379).

Itinerary 7. Dover East Cliff to St Margaret's at Cliffe.

To many, the itinerary from Dover eastwards is the classic white chalk section. It is entirely in Upper Chalk (as redefined at the base of the Lewes Chalk). It is possible to walk the section from Dover Priory station to the East Cliff and then down Langdon Stairs to the beach. A falling tide is essential. There is one very

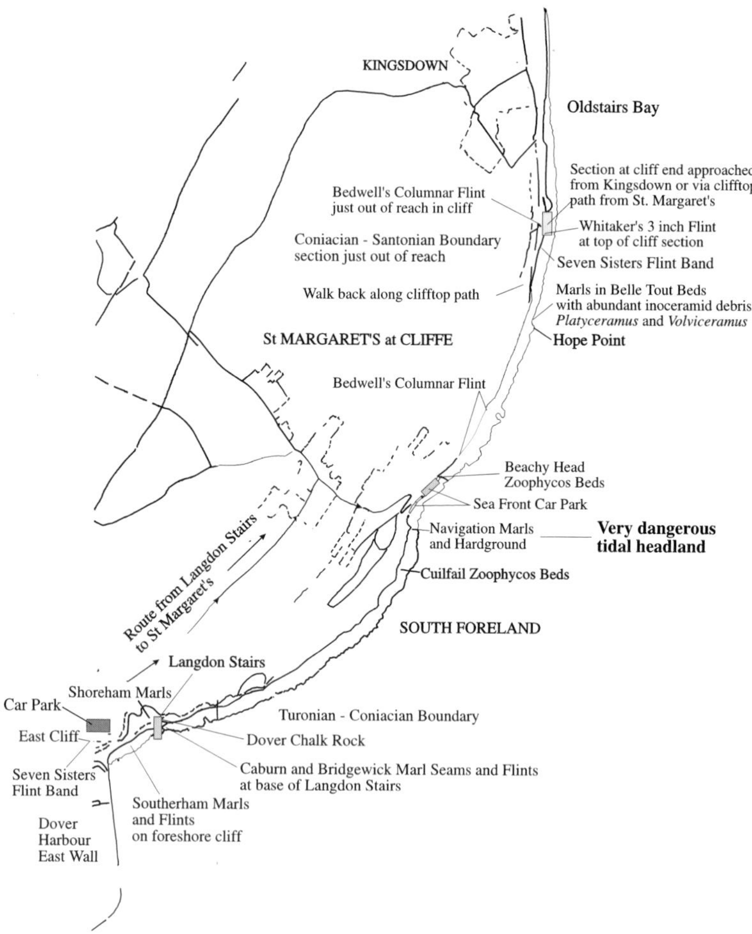

Figure 56. Map for Itinerary 7, the traverse from East Cliff, Dover via Langdon Stairs and St Margaret's at Cliffe to Kingsdown (Deal), and back along the cliff top path.

critical part of the itinerary with respect to tides, Ness Point on the south side of St. Margaret's at Cliffe. **This can only be rounded at low tide and is extremely dangerous on a rising tide, once the water is covering the rock platform.**

Locality l. The East Cliff and Langdon Stairs (TR 334422).

Summary of geological interest

Seven Sisters Flint Band, Cuckmere Beds, key marker beds,
Southerham Marls, boundary between Lewes and Seaford Chalks,
Zoophycos horizons, Dover Chalk Rock,
Caburn Sponge Bed, type locality for *Inoceramus lamarcki.*

Vehicles can be parked at the East Cliff viewing point (TR 334422) which provides a fine vista over Dover Harbour and the white cliffs (Figure 56).

The walk through Dover eastwards along East Cliff Road and Athol Terrace up the East Cliff path under the A2 is rewarding (Figure 57) as beds below those exposed at the base of Langdon Stairs can be seen. This is especially important as the change from massive New Pit Chalk to the nodular Lewes Chalk with regular seams of flint is seen at Athol Terrace before going eastwards under the A2. Typical Lewes Chalk bands of red, iron-stained nodular layers stand-out in

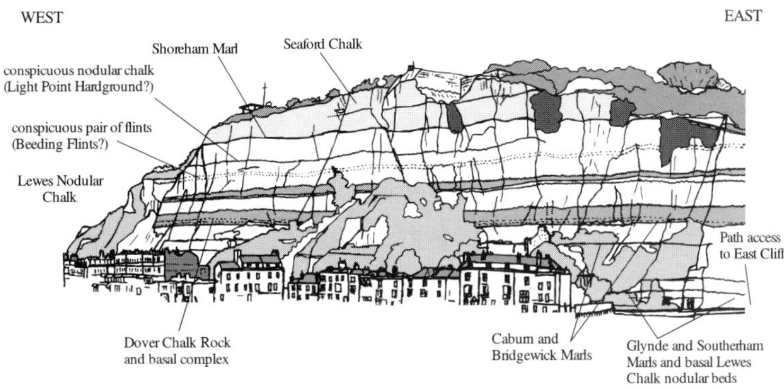

Figure 57. Sketch from a photograph of the White Chalk cliffs on the east side of Dover beneath Dover Castle. Each of the main markers indicated are present along the access path leading eastwards under the A2 trunk road to East Cliff. The basal beds of the Lewes Chalk are well exposed, showing both nodular chalk and flints between the Glynde and Southerham Marls. Nodular chalk layers and flint bands are particularly conspicuous in this cliff face.

the cliff above. Marl seams are conspicuous grooves in the cliff The first nodular chalk layers of the Lewes Chalk (and hence the base of the Upper Chalk) are seen here, but are below the base of the Langdon Stairs section.

From the east side of the A2, exposures are relatively poor but the path climbs across the stratigraphy into the Seaford Chalk. One conspicuous semi-continuous flint band is a marker in the path wall. This is the Seven Sisters Flint Band of Sussex (Mortimore, 1979, 1980, 1983, 1986: East Cliff Semitabular of Smith & Gale, 1982; Oldstairs Bay Flint of Robinson, 1986). This flint has the same association of *Platyceramus* and *Volviceramus* below, in and above as in Sussex at Birling Gap and Tarring Neville.

Follow the track eastwards (Figure 56) to the amphitheatre set in the cliffs that is Langdon Hole (the head of a truncated valley). Langdon Stairs zig-zag down the cliff to the beach (Figures 58 & 59). The exposed chalk begins in the Cuckmere Beds of the Seaford Chalk, the Seven Sisters Flint Band (SSFB) recurs towards the top of the 75 m section (Figures 60-62). Then each of the key marker beds Southerham Marls and Flints at beach level can be followed downwards. Below the SSFB, beds with abundant shell debris of *Platyceramus* and/or *Volviceramus* are often associated with thin marly complexes, each marl complex correlates with the simlar Belle Tout Marls of the Sussex stratigraphy. Some 17 m below the SSFB the Shoreham Marls are present at the boundary between the Lewes and Seaford Chalks. Bands of red, iron-stained nodular Lewes Chalk contrast with the purer, white more homogeneous Seaford Chalk. This contrasting lithology leads to contrasting rubbly brash (Lewes Chalk) and slabby brash (Seaford Chalk) in ploughed fields and is used by BGS for mapping the boundary. A composite section is constructed from the East Cliff and Langdon Steps exposures (Figures 61 & 62). This is also the boundary between the conventional *Micraster cortestudinarium* and *M. coranguinum* zones around the Lower - Middle Coniacian boundary.

The flints between the Shoreham Marls contain a further marker layer with tubes and fingers, usually also recovered in core. Below the Shoreham Marls *Zoophycos* is conspicuous and stratigraphically consistent with St Margaret's at Cliffe, Thurrock (Mortimore, Roberts & Jones, 1990) and with Beachy Head (the Beachy Head Zoophycos Beds). These beds also contain large *Cremnoceramus crassus.*

A further conspicuous horizon of *Zoophycos* is present below the Navigation Hardgrounds which represent the 'Dover Top Rock' (Mortimore, 1983; Bailey *et al.,* 1983, 1984). This level is broadly at the Turonian - Coniacian boundary

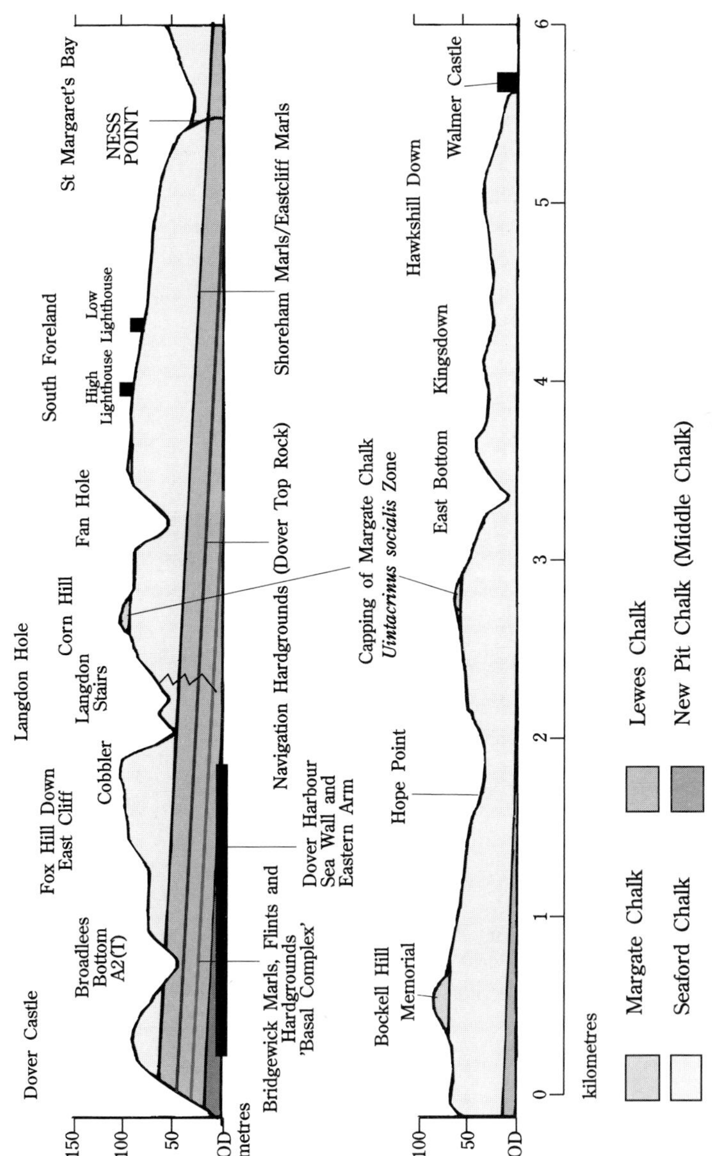

Figure 58. Schematic long-section of the Middle and Upper Chalk cliffs between Dover and Kingsdown, Kent. (Modified from Sherborne in Rowe (1900); and Shephard-Thorn (1988).

although the exact limits remain to be determined. A very poorly preserved ammonite, *Forresteria petrocoriense,* was found inside a broken echinoid on the top surface of the Navigation Hardground on Langdon Stairs and has been used to suggest that this surface is the base of the Coniacian.

Of particular interest is the level of the Dover Chalk Rock. This comprises a series of hardgrounds (Figure 60) with the lower ones, in particular, containing three different assemblages of ammonites. The bottom nodular layer contains

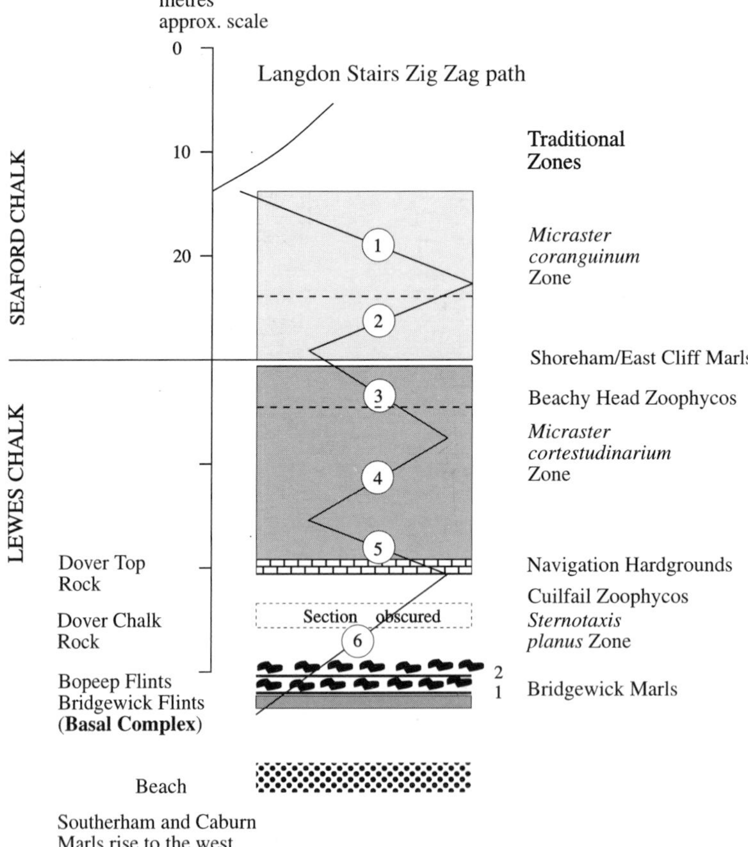

Figure 59. Positions of key marker beds in the Upper Chalk in relation to the Langdon Stairs zig zag path. (Modified from Rowe, 1900; and Shephard-Thorn, 1988).

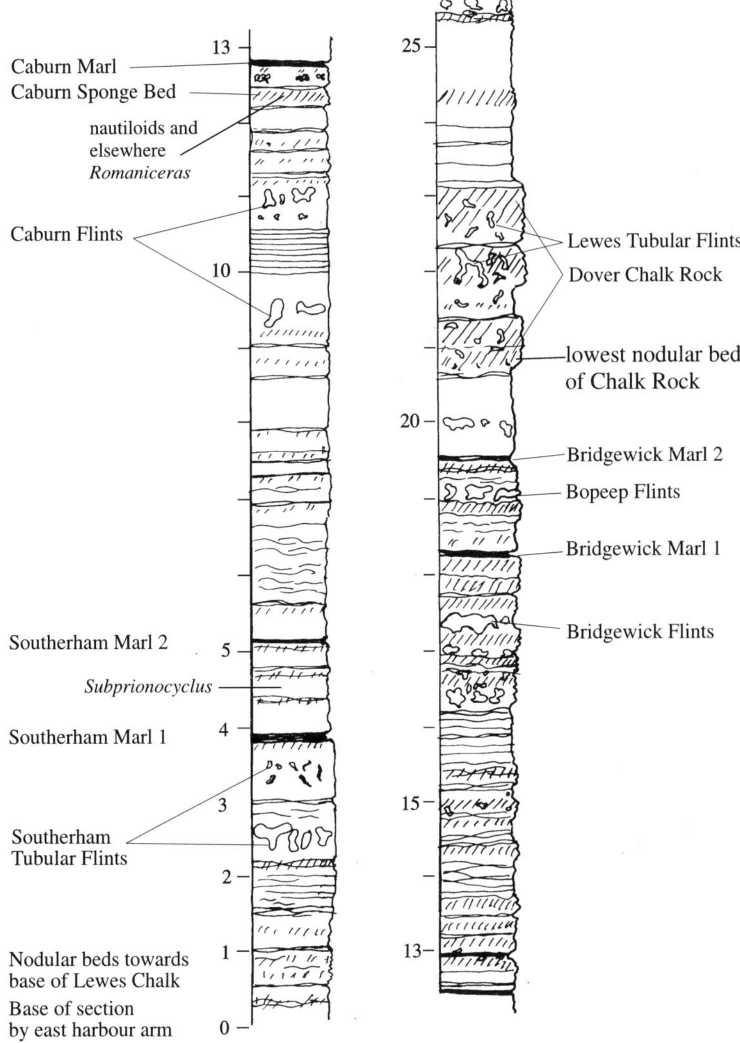

Figure 60. Lower Lewes Chalk at Langdon Stairs. Lowest beds are repeated along the cliffs beneath Dover Castle, opposite the harbour, and at the top of Aker's Steps. Higher beds are repeated east of Langdon Stairs along the beach. Mostly Upper Turonian (topmost Terebratulina lata and the Sternotaxis plana zones).

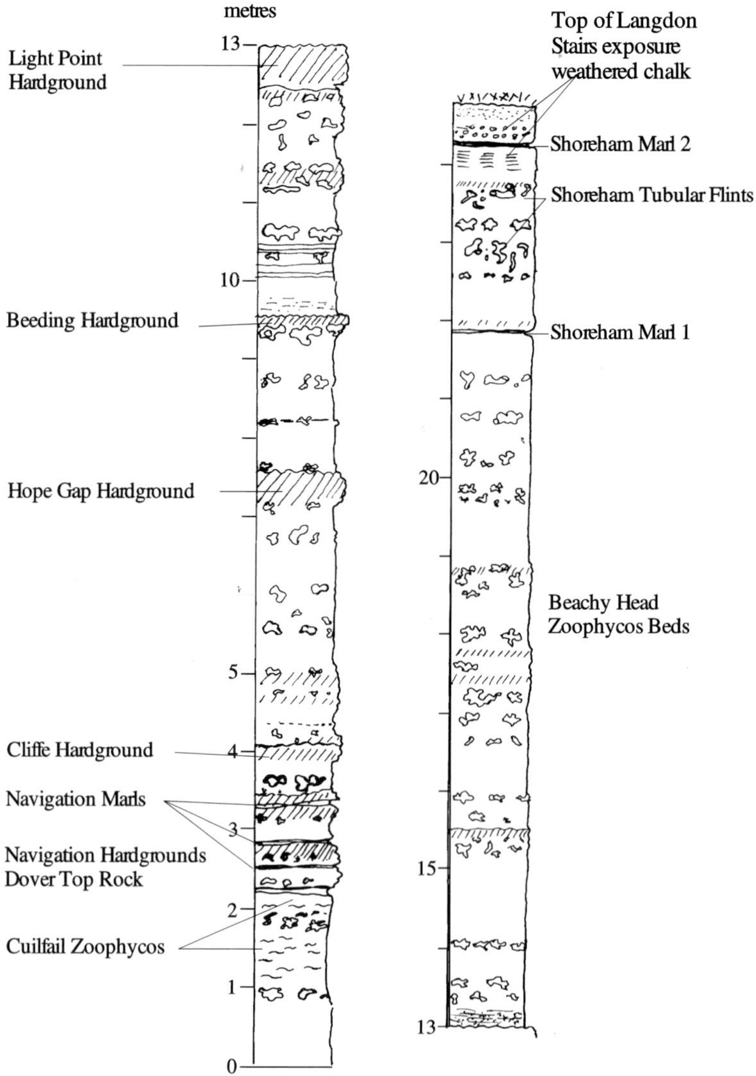

Figure 61. Upper Lewes Chalk at Langdon Stairs. These beds are repeated at Frenchman's Fall and northeastwards towards St. Margaret's at Cliffe and the north side of St. Margaret's Bay. Highest Turonian and Lower Coniacian Micraster cortestudinarium *zone (divided into a lower* M. normanniae *zone, a middle* M. decipiens *zone and an upper* M. turonensis *zone).*

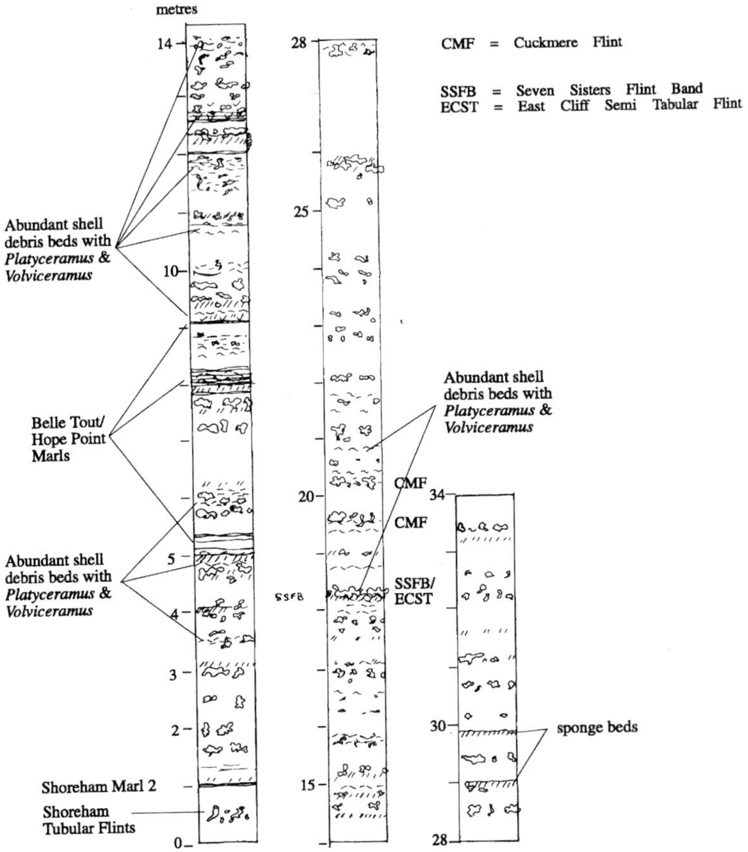

Figure 62. Seaford Chalk at Langdon Stairs - Langdon Cliffs - East Cliff. These same beds occur northwards from St. Margaret's Bay to Kingsdown and again just overlap at the top with the Thanet coast sections (Figure 66).

Subprionocyclus hitchinensis and *Yezoites bladenensis* but no *Hyphantoceras* (low diversity). Nodular beds 2 and 3 are higher diversity containing *Hyphantoceras reussianum* and lots of small bivalves and gastropods. Then in the top bed *Mytiloides incertus* is present. At Dover this represents a condensation in the Kingston Beds and around the Lewes Marl. The Lewes Marl is occluded, but the characteristic Lewes Tubular Flints are still present in beds with *Micraster leskei, Mytiloides striatoconcentricus* and typical Chalk Rock brachiopods. It is called the 'Dover Chalk Rock' because these beds only represent the upper part of the complete Chalk Rock of Berkshire-Wiltshire (Bromley & Gale, 1982).

Beneath the Dover Chalk Rock is the pair of Bridgewick Marls and the most conspicuous flint bands in the Kent Chalk (Figure 63 & rear cover, lower basal complex of Jukes-Browne & Hill, 1903). These Bridgewick Marls and Flints were taken by the British Geological Survey as the base of the former Upper Chalk in the North Downs (Holmes pers. comm in Mortimore, 1987; Mortimore & Wood, 1986). This basal complex and overlying stratigraphy is repeated in wonderful sections at beach level to the east of the steps.

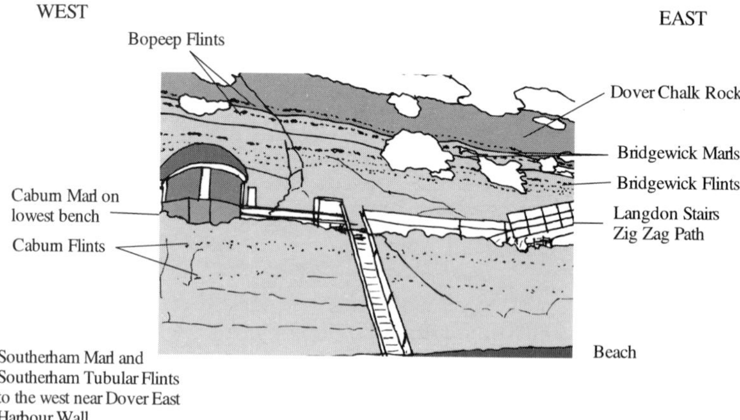

Figure 63. Sketch of the so-called 'Basal Complex' at Langdon Stairs which includes the Bridgewick Flints, Bridgewick Marls and Bopeep Flints. This complex was taken as the former mapping base of the Upper Chalk shown on old British Geological Survey maps.

On the last bench before beach level the Caburn Marl with underlying Caburn Sponge Bed and flints is present. The surface beneath this marl has yielded nautiloids, *Romaniceras deverianum* (elsewhere) and *Micraster (Epiaster) michelini,* the same level for this *Micraster* as the Caburn Pit examples in Sussex, but *Bicavea rotaformis* has not yet been recorded from Kent. The flints between the marl and the tough nodular bed are small, pink and characteristically carious, a further example of a lithological combination used for correlation.

At beach level, against the East Harbour Wall, the two Southerham Marls and underlying Southerham Tubular Flints are usually exposed. This is the type locality of *Inoceramus lamarcki* obtained from the large Southerham Flints at Langdon Stairs. Again the Southerham Marl 1 is a conspicuous, plastic marl with abundant *Coskinophragma* and the underlying flints retain their characteristic Sussex mixed small and large sizes, and tubular or finger flint character.

Locality 2. Langdon Bay (TR 344424), **Fan Bay** (TR 355427) and **South Foreland** (TR 363433).

Summary of geological interest

The Dover Chalk Rock, giant Paramoudra flints, Cuilfail Zoophycos, Navigation Hardgrounds: Turonian - Coniacian boundary.

If the intention is to walk this section to St Margaret's Bay then a **falling tide is essential** and Ness Point (TR 368443) at the exit into St Margaret's Bay must be passed within two hours of low tide. The walk can be tough on shoes and ankles (seaweed covered boulders are very slippery and sharp) and care also needs to be taken at the Langdon Bay end of the walk as high tide can cut-off the unwary. Once in Fan Bay it is possible to sit out normal tides (not high Spring tides). It is, however, a magnificent section and will reward the intrepid with clean, wave-washed, highly fossiliferous sections. The Dover Chalk Rock is wonderfully exposed for a long section and individual beds can be studied and fossils collected and compared with Langdon Stairs. Lateral variations such as the cutting out of Bridgewick Marl 1 on a hardground and the virtual disappearance of the Navigation Marls. The numerous fallen blocks yield *Micraster, Echinocorys* and inoceramids from the Caburn Marl to Bedwell's Columnar Flint. Fallen flints include giant Paramoudras from Bedwell's Columnar Flint and below. The Cuilfail Zoophycos, again wonderfully exposed, occur as mm thin wisps of marl, and the Navigation Hardgrounds are also repeated eastwards towards Ness Point. Ness Point wave-cut platform is formed along the surface of the Navigation Hardgrounds. Of particular stratigraphic importance to fixing the Turonian - Coniacian boundary is the record of a *Didymotis* collected between two of the Navigation Hardgrounds (Lee, unpublished). The two main events (concentrations) of this fossil, recognised in Spain, Germany and the Czech Republic, are in the Upper Turonian but the fossil ranges into the Lower Coniacian.

Locality 3. St Margaret's at Cliffe (TR 368445) **to Kingsdown** (TR 381472).

Summary of geological interest

Beachy Head Zoophycos Beds, Seven Sisters Flint Band and Bedwell's Columnar Flint, Lewes Chalk hardgrounds, Shoreham Marls.

The pub on the seafront by the car park at St Margaret's at Cliffe offers a break before completing the Dover Coast sections to Kingsdown. Vehicles can also be parked on the seafront. If the intention is to walk southwards round the South Foreland then **the same warnings about the tide on Ness Point apply** as before. Once the tide reaches the level of the rock platform it moves across the platform very quickly. Listen for the change in the sound of the waves.

Rowe (1900) identified his *M. cortestudinarium - M. coranguinum* boundary at the sheet flints seen in the cliffs on the south side of St. Margaret's Bay. This was significantly lower than his boundary at East Cliff-Langdon which was at the nodular chalks above the Shoreham Marls. This boundary is now difficult of access. Most of the cliff is in the upper Lewes Chalk.

The walk from the north side of St Margaret's to Kingsdown can take at least a further 2 hours and requires a low tide (preferably a falling tide). **There is only one escape point along the route** (Figure 56). On the north side of St Margaret's Bay, standing on the sea wall, the streaky chalk of the Beachy Head Zoophycos Beds is superbly exposed. Looking carefully at the millimetre-thick dark grey streaks it can be seen that they are within the lighter grey fills of *Thalassinoides* burrows. Grooves and subhorizontal overbreaks in the cliff are associated with the Shoreham and Belle Tout Marls. Standing back from the cliffs and looking towards the crest line the grouping of the flint bands at the Conician-Santonian boundary is directly comparable with those in Sussex at Seaford Head (compare with Figure 33). The Seven Sisters Flint Band and Bedwell's Columnar Flint can be identified as the main band of black flints below.

Walking north on the beach the nodular chalks and hardgrounds in the upper Lewes Chalk progressively dip across the wave-cut platform. Some these beds develop typical green glauconitic, phosphatic and bored surfaces (e.g. the Light Point Hardground). Higher beds are brought to beach level by the gentle dip providing long sections for collecting. In particular there are common *Micraster* in the Shoreham Marls and inoceramids in the Belle Tout Beds. A fossil that is rare in Sussex, *Conulus raulini,* is common in Kent particularly between two of the Belle Tout Marls 1 and 2.

The Shoreham Marls are accessible at The Cut and the Belle Tout/Hope Point

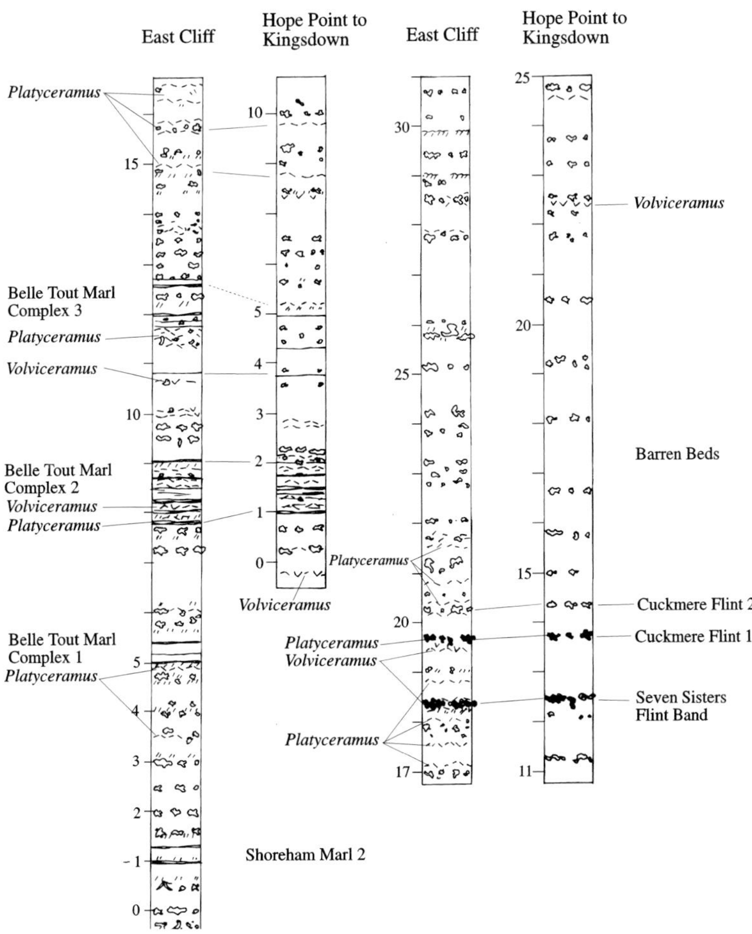

Figure 64. Correlation of the Seaford Chalk sections at East Cliff, Dover with those between Hope Point and Kingsdown (Deal). Note that both flints and marl seams become less well developed northwards.

Mails around Hope Point. The SSFB is accessible at the southern end of the rifle ranges at Kingsdown but Bedwell's Columnar Flint, although easily recognisable, is inaccessible without ladders. The section (Figure 64) indicates the key features to look for.

Having completed this section there is a wonderful, peaceful walk back to Dover along the cliff-top path to St. Margaret's at Cliffe, past the Bleriot Memorial and past the Strait of Dover main coastguard lookout.

Itinerary 8. The Isle of Thanet

The Isle of Thanet coastal sections of north Kent expose the stratigraphically highest chalk of the North Downs, the Margate Chalk. This contrasts with the same age beds in Sussex by having no marl seams and no or reduced flint seams. Those flint bands that do occur are, therefore, more conspicuous. There are several biostratigraphical differences between Thanet and Sussex in the distribution and/or abundance of belemnites, brachiopods and the crinoids (Mortimore, 1979, 1986). The distribution of the Chalk zones in Thanet is given in the Dover and Ramsgate BGS Memoir (Shephard-Thorn, 1988, fig. 11) and during the course of the BGS remapping up to 6 m of *Offaster pilula* Zone chalk was proved in a pit at Broadstairs (TR 384686).

Rowe (1900, p. 94) commented on the relative safety of these Thanet sections. *'In the case of the Thanet coast the danger of being caught by the tide is very small. Many parts can be worked even at high tide, and the "gaps" on the shore are so numerous that escape can be easily made. The only really dangerous place is west of Collin's Gap, between Margate and Westgate, and at the east end of Westgate itself. Here the tide rises very high, and comes up with great speed. Two other places to be mentioned are White Ness, at the east side of Kingsgate, and the section between Ramgate and Pegwell, where there are no gaps, and where the shore is in places of a very soft and treacherous nature.'*

Rowe's comments still stand, but sadly sea walls have since been constructed around much of the coast at Dumpton Gap, Broadstairs, Joss Bay, Foreness Point and along much of the North coast reducing especially the exposure of *Marsupites* and *Uintacrinus* chalk. Extension of Ramsgate Harbour by land reclamation into Pegwell Bay has also reduced the exposure of Seaford Chalk, but the undercliff road is still just workable. Quicksands are still a hazard in Pegwell Bay. The relatively new undersea walls do, however, mean that cliff erosion is reduced and levels formerly difficult to study are now accessible. For example, Bedwell's Columnar Flint is within reach along the top of the sea wall going north from Dumpton Gap.

Erosion of the cliffs and chalk platform, storms and construction all change the exposures and their safety aspects. It is always advisable to carry out a quick reconnaissance of access and escape points.

Sherborne (in Rowe, 1900, Section 3, p.368) and Shephard-Thorn (1988, fig. 12), provide invaluable long-sections of the cliffs as a guide. The excursion begins in Pegwell Bay, but again is designed so that each section can be taken individually and more time can be spent at each location.

Locality 1. Ramsgate (TR 351652) **to Pegwell Bay** (TR 351652).

Summary of geological interest

Quaternary, Tertiary beds; faulted high Seaford Chalk and almost flintless Margate Chalk.

If travelling by public transport then it is easier to start the excursion in Ramsgate and walk from the harbour to Pegwell Bay (Figures 65 to 66). Vehicles can be parked along the cliff top (TR 370642) or parking is possible on the undercliff road via the ferry-port road. (When the Ramsgate Harbour Tunnel and the new harbour access road have been constructed this parking area may not exist). Access to the western undercliff from the cliff top is via several paths or steps. From the ramp at the eastern end of the undercliff (Jacob's Ladder) the key marker bed is Bedwell's Columnar Flint with associated abundant wave-like sheets of shelly fragments of *Cladoceramus undulatoplicatus,* the basal Santonian index fossil. Although the apparent dip is westwards, faults keep this flint in the cliff as far as the western end of the undercliff (Figures 67 & 70). This part of the chalk stratigraphy is now better exposed in the cliffs from Dumpton Gap to Broadstairs and just south of the North Foreland (see below).

At the western end of the undercliff wall, beds above Bedwell's Columnar Flint including Whitaker's Three Inch Flint and Barrois' Sponge Bed a red, iron-stained nodular, sponge bed, occur in a very faulted section. Westwards, these higher two beds dip towards beach level in the section (with a sea wall) and, depending on condition of the beach, the Barrois' Sponge Bed and overlying *Conulus* bed and then the *Uintacrinus socialis* chalk with very few flints can be studied (see also Joss Bay). Bedwell's Columnar Flint with abundant *Cladoceramus undulatoplicatus* is present just above beach level in the first sea-worn cliff exposures at the end of the Western Undercliff Wall (Figure 70). Large domed forms of *Micraster (Isomicraster) gibbus* occur in the wave-cut platform in beds below Bedwell's Columnar Flint in association with other indices of the basal

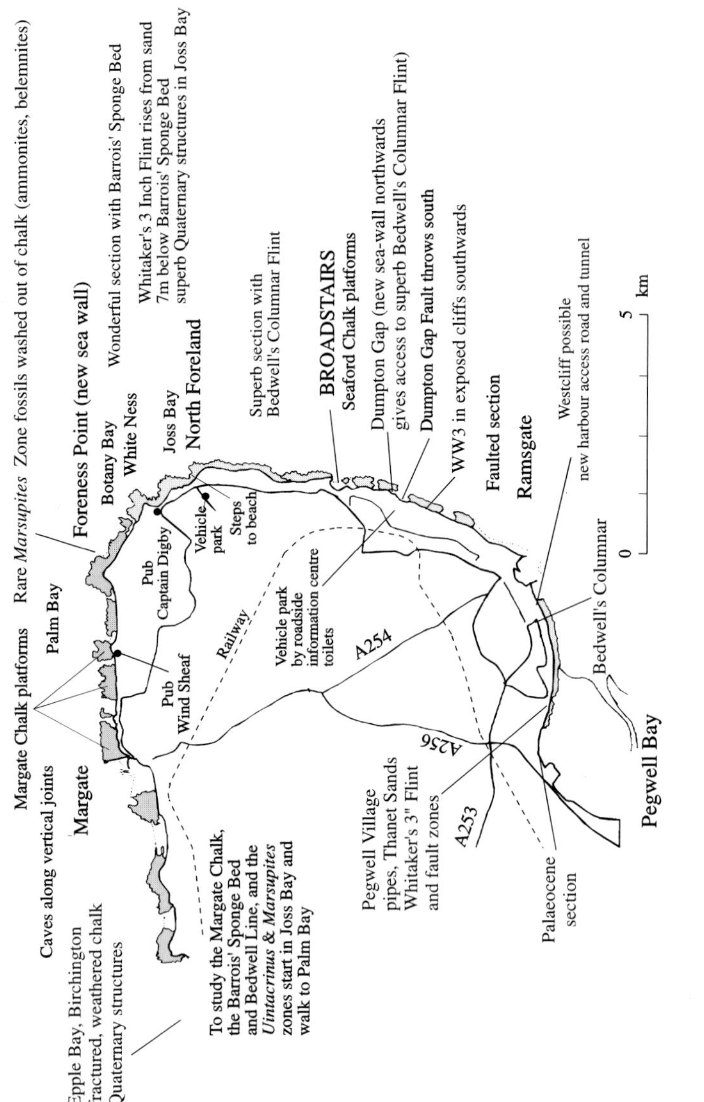

Figure 65. Map of the Isle of Thanet Upper Chalk, Palaeocene and Quaternary localities. The western end of Pegwell Bay contains Quaternary loess and solifluction lobes overlying Palaeocene deposits and Chalk cliffs (Margate Member). Ramsgate's New Harbour Access Road and Tunnel may be built in the near future, changing the exposures available on the Westcliff undercliff walk.

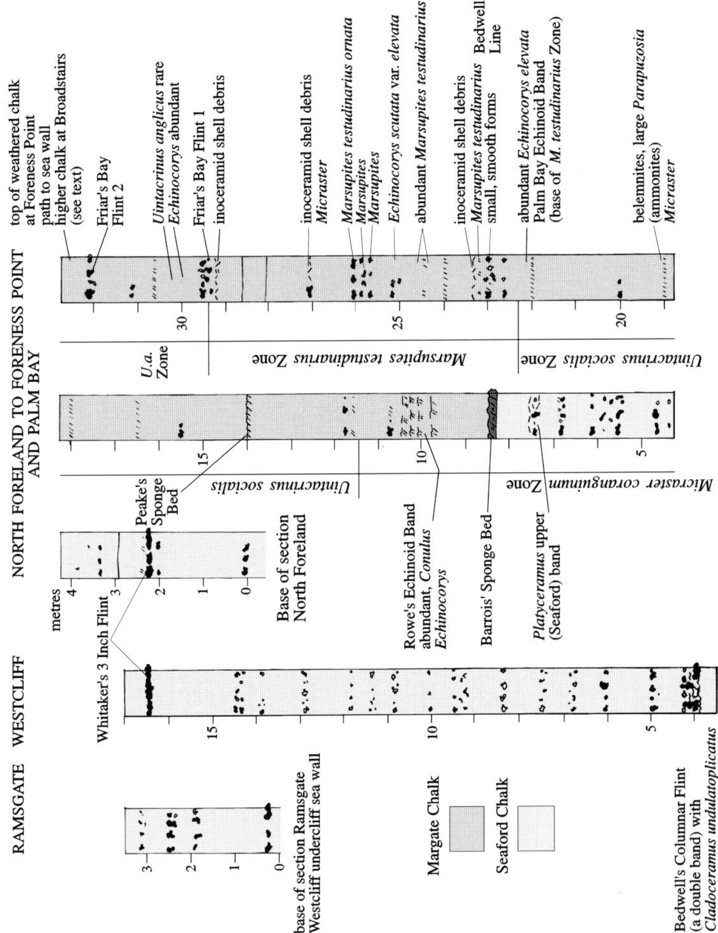

Figure 66. Seaford and Margate Chalk Members of the Upper Chalk Formation in the Isle of Thanet coastal exposures from Ramsgate Westcliff to Margate. The Ramsgate and North Foreland sections are linked by correlation of Whitaker's Three Inch Flint Band.

Santonian, including the barrel-shaped columnals and calyces of the crinoid *Bourgueticrinus* and the brachiopod *Gibbithyris ellipsoidalis*.

Walking westwards the small, finger and tubular-like, rather scattered flints (some related to the trace fossil *Zoophycos*), in beds between Bedwell's Columnar Flint and Whitaker's Three Inch Flint Band come down to beach level.

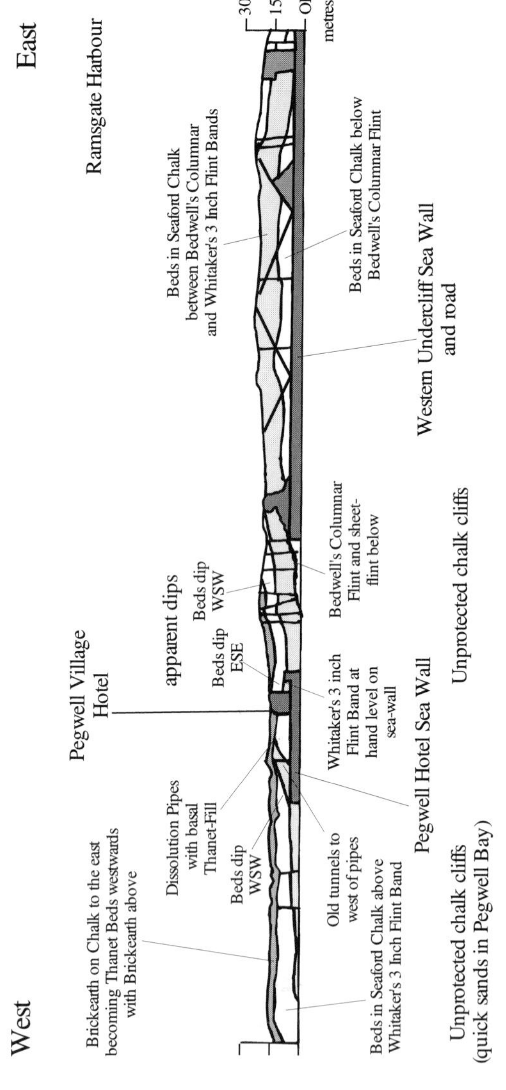

Figure 67. Sketch section of Chalk cliffs from Ramsgate to Pegwell Bay showing the position of main faults (most faults are zones of fracturing 0.3 m to 5 m wide). Subhorizontal joints related to penecontemporaneous slide planes are common, hence the sheet flint below the Bedwell's Columnar Flint (modified from Shephard-Thorn, 1988).

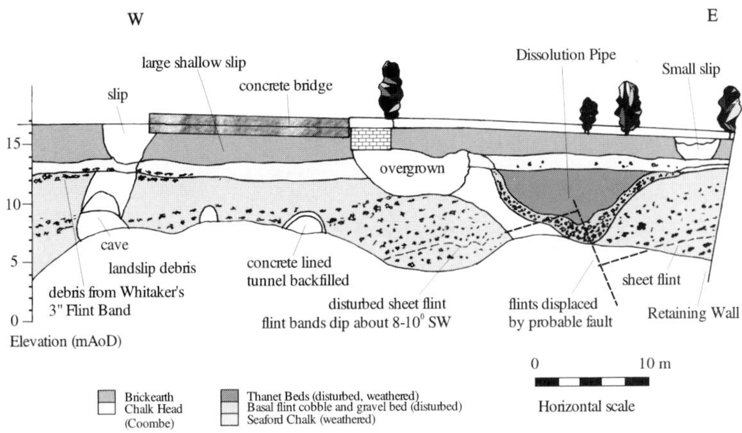

Figure 68. Sketch geological section of Chalk cliffs adjacent to Pegwell Bay Hotel, looking north.

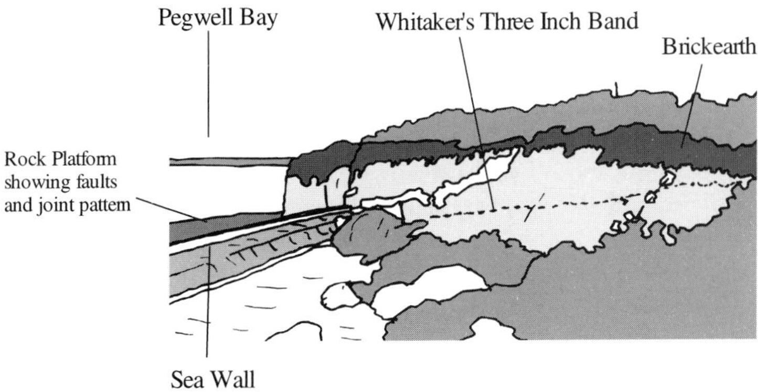

Figure 69. Sketch of the cliff exposure looking west into Pegwell Bay from Pegwell village Hotel showing Whitaker's Three Inch Flint Band dipping at about 8° south.

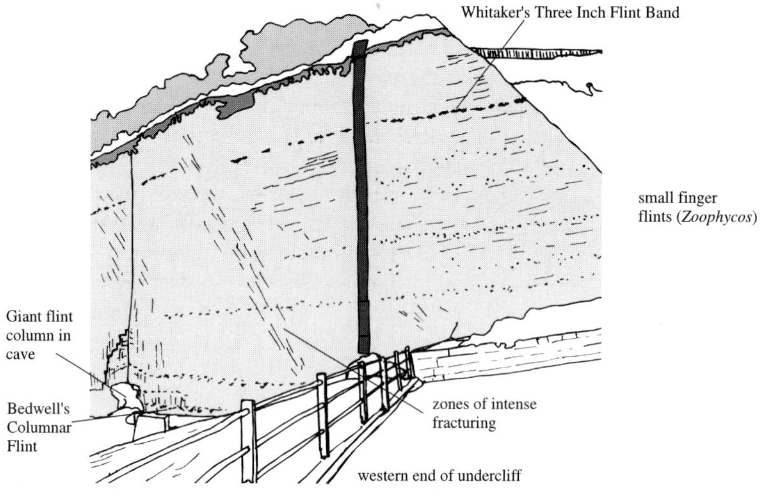

Figure 70. Sketch of the 18 m high cliff exposure at the western end of Ramsgate's western undercliff road showing the position of Bedwell's Columnar Flint, Whitaker's Three Inch Flint and faults, with intense jointing typical of the Thanet area.

The sense of movement on the numerous faults with fracture zones is easily identified by the offset of the Whitaker's Three Inch Flint. This latter flint band only becomes accessible on top of the short stretch of sea-wall beneath Pegwell Bay Hotel. Here, numerous fossils including examples of late forms of the bivalve *Platyceramus*, associated with *Sphenoceramus* and *Conulus albogalerus* are present. There is also a very rich mesofauna. The cave and sets of steps on this bit of sea-wall have been closed. Immediately west of Pegwell village is an embayment in the cliff-line, now protected by a further sea-wall. The cliff is weathered and covered in vegetation but contains a large dissolution pipe, filled with basal Thanet Sands and underlying flint-cobble and gravel bed. Closed or filled tunnels and caves are also present (Figure. 68). The Chalk is dipping surprisingly steeply (about 8°) to the SSW, picked out by Whitaker's Three Inch Flint Band (Figure. 69). Red to brown brickearths cap the chalk cliffs at this point. At the western end of the embayment, Whitaker's Three Inch Flint has dipped below the wall and the relatively flintless Margate Chalk above forms the cliffs (Figures 66 & 67).

An unconformable contact between the Thanet Beds and the Upper Chalk (Margate Chalk Member, *Marsupites testudinarius* Zone) is well exposed at Redcliff Point (TR 353643) at the north western end of Pegwell Bay. A marly layer, the Frinsbury Clay, is present between the Chalk and the basal Bullhead Bed, and was once thought to be possibly Maastrichtian. This clay is very thin at Pegwell Bay but thickens towards Richborough. There is also a sheet flint of controversial origin at the contact between the Chalk and overlying beds (is it a Chalk flint or of much later origin?). The basal Thanet Bullhead Bed (flint conglomerate of green and black-coated, angular and rounded flints set in a dark green, glauconitic sandy marl) is only 150 mm thick in contrast to the 400-500 mm thickness of the basal Tertiary Bullhead bed at Newhaven. This basal bed is overlain by fine green, sandy marls (Cliffsend Greensand Bed), alternating clays and silty clays (Stourmouth Clays), dark, greenish-grey marls (Pegwell Marls), and yellowish grey, fine silty sands (Reculver Silts).

The Quaternary loess (TR 350652) resting on Thanet Beds northeast of Cliffsend, Pegwell Bay was described by Pitcher, Shearman and Pugh (1954) and compared with Iranian loess by Fookes & Best (1969). Its mostly silt-sized quartz grains make it stable when dry but unstable when wet. The loess was quarried for brickmaking and its characteristic, regular, vertical joints are well seen here. Periglacial solifluction deposits are also present.

The section ends by the former hoverport. Should a walk back along the beach to Ramsgate be contemplated beware of the tide. There is a makeshift access at the western end of the Pegwell village seawall across, slippery, seaweed covered boulders. Permission needs to be obtained from Pegwell Bay Hotel to gain access to this embayment but it is worth a visit, and the Pub bar overlooks the Bay.

Locality 2. Dumpton Gap, Broadstairs (TR 396666).

Summary of geological interest

Bedwell's Columnar Flint; basal Santonian index fossil assemblage.

Broadstairs beach is a very popular spot and a peaceful study of the Chalk cliffs can be undertaken only in the off season! Parking can be found along the edge of the minor road above Dumpton Gap, and the access to the sea-wall and beach is in the centre of the bay. Toilets and a kiosk are also present. The section is heavily faulted either side of the access point to the beach. Whitaker's Three Inch Flint and Barrois' Sponge Bed are in the cliffs to the south but Bedwell's Columnar Flint is low in the cliffs to the north, along the top of the sea-wall, with Whitaker's Three Inch Flint barely visible at times in the top of the cliff (Figures 71 & 72).

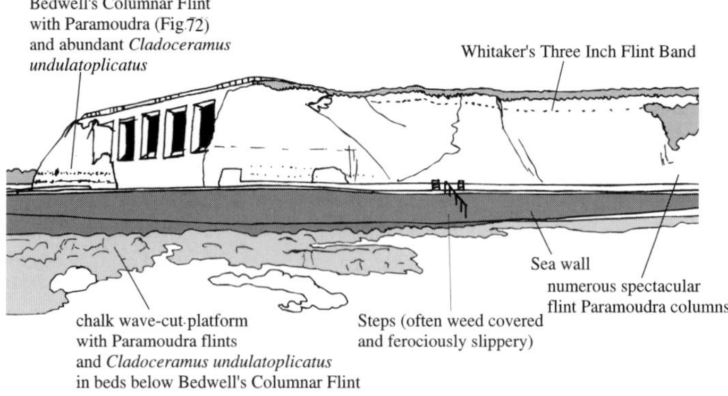

Figure 71. Sketch of the cliff exposures on the north side of Dumpton Gap showing the position of Bedwell's Columnar and Whitaker's Three Inch Flint bands.

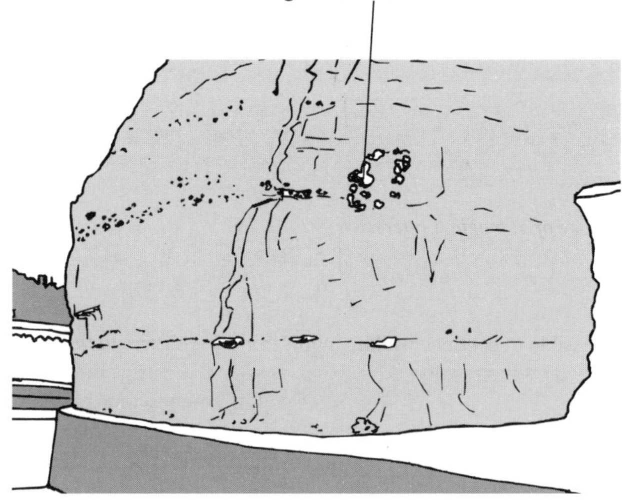

Figure 72. Sketch of a close up of a Paramoudra flint developed in Bedwell's Columnar Flint (position indicated on Figure 71).

This is perhaps the best section for Bedwell's Columnar Flint and should not be missed. Identification of this flint is relatively simple. It is a conspicuous line of double flints with occasional vertical columns of flint. The vertical columns have been related to flint forming around a special trace fossil *Bathichnus paramoudrae* (Bromley, Schulz & Peake, 1975; Clayton, 1986). Such vertical columns are called Paramoudras. Bedwell's Columnar Flint is associated with an abundance of the inoceramid bivalve *Cladoceramus undulatoplicatus.* This bivalve has a characteristic wavy outline in section and pink colour in contrast to the flat, thicker, predominantly grey-coloured prismatic shells of *Platyceramus.* A long length of section dipping gently northwards reveals many columnar flints in this band and yields other elements of the basal Santonian index fossil assemblage including *Gibbythyris ellipsoidalis, Orbirhynchia pisiformis,* large very thin shelled *Sternotaxis, Micraster (Isomicraster) gibbus* (large, highly domed forms) and special forms of the crinoid *Bourgueticrinus* (barrel-shaped). The entry of *Cladoceramus undulatoplicatus* is taken as the base of the Santonian and this occurs below Bedwell's Columnar Flint (see Beachy Head and Seaford excursions, and Bailey *et al.,* 1983). In the wave-cut platform fronting the sea-wall on the north side of Dumpton Gap a further band of well developed nodular-flint band with some columns is present (seen at low tide). This second, lower columnar-flint, is also associated with *Cladoceramus undulatoplicatus* and is probably equivalent to the Chartham Flint of the Stour valley near Canterbury and the Michel Dean Flint of Sussex. The Dumpton Gap exposures demonstrate that more than one flint may contain columns, even on the Kent coast.

Locality 3. Dumpton Gap via North Foreland, Joss Bay and Botany Bay to Foreness Point (TR 384716).

Summary of geological interest

Whitaker' Three Inch Flint, Barrois' Sponge Bed, Rowe's Echinoid Band, the Bedwell Line flints.

It is possible to continue walking north from Broadstairs to the North Foreland. Those with vehicles will find it more convenient to return and drive to Joss Bay (Figure 65). Parking is possible in the pay-park on top of the cliffs or along the road opposite the track and steps to Joss Bay. Whitaker's Three Inch Flint Band passes through the level of the gully giving access to the beach and dips northwards to beach level. Whitaker's Three Inch Flint contrasts with Bedwell's Columnar in being a nearly solid and continuous, single tabular flint. It is also a major boundary in the biostratigraphy with a significant turnover in foraminifera (Bailey *et al.,* 1983), a concentration level for echinoids and inoceramid bivalves including *Cordiceramus* and *Sphenoceramus* (Mortimore, 1986). Why should the key marker flints (secondary, diagenetic features) also be associated with significant biostratigraphic turnovers?

Those interested in the structure of the chalk should note the characteristic joint sets which were studied here by Middlemiss (1983). Hutchinson (in Hoek & Bray, 1980) used the cliff failures in Joss Bay to calculate the shear strength of chalk joints and factors of safety against failure of white chalk slopes. There are also excellent Quaternary structures in the cliff-top sediments capping the chalk in and around the access ramp to the beach. Whitaker's Three Inch Flint has been fragmented (by freeze-thaw?) and churned so that fragments are crudely aligned in involutions. These thermocast features are present on many parts of the Thanet coast, but are particularly conspicuous here and at Birchington on the north coast. Some probably represent patterned ground stone stripes now covered by more recent sediments.

Continuing northwards from Dumpton Gap, Barrois' Sponge Bed, a conspicuous 200-300 mm thick red, iron-stained nodular sponge bed, dips to beach level often forming a small reef on the chalk wave-cut platform. This is again a key marker bed throughout much of the basin being strongly developed over structural highs. It is present at Clandon, Surrey (where it is called the Clandon Hardground), and forms the floor of Chislehurst Caves. It is also extremely well developed at pits like North Barn, near Dorchester, Dorset (where it is a true hardground). This Sponge Bed appears to be absent at other localities in local troughs such as Pinden in the North Downs. Walking along this surface on the rock platform the most conspicuous fossils are the large, tea-cosy-shaped *Echinocorys* on and in the Sponge Bed and commonly occurring unusual large *Micraster* (not *M. coranguinum*). Barrois' Sponge Bed is taken as the boundary between the flinty Seaford Chalk below and the relatively flintless Margate Chalk above.

Another significant bioevent is recognised above Barrois' Sponge Bed, Rowe's Echinoid Band (Figure 66). This band is characterised by an abundance of *Conulus albogalerus* with *Cretirhynchia plicatilis,* but at places like Pepper Hill in the North Downs *Echinocorys* is also common and the echinoids are generally more abundant. The boundary between the *Micraster coranguinum* and *Uintacrinus socialis* zones is taken just above Rowe's Echinoid Band where *U. socialis* first enters.

For a long length of coast beyond this point the chalk is almost flintless and devoid of conspicuous, continuous markers making measurement of the sections difficult. Flints occur in occasional patches and the only satisfactory measurements that can be made use expanding surveyors staffs which are stretched vertically across the cliff between identifiable marker beds.

Flints return towards Foreness Point and again the first conspicuous broad seam of flints, the Bedwell Line (Figure 66), is closely associated with another fossil turnover, the entry of *Marsupites testudinarius* and abundant *Echinocorys elevata.* The wave-cut platform in the beds below the Bedwell Line yield both large ammonites, *Parapuzosia,* (as a line of ammonites recorded by Bedwell 1874) and belemnites, *Actinocamax verus* and occasional *Gonioteuthis* (Bailey *et al.*, 1983). Several *Belemnellocamax grossuveri* have been found washed out of the top of the *U. socialis* Zone on the rock platform.

Construction of a sea wall has partly obscured some of the best sections around Foreness Point and Palm Bay. In the chalk walls along the access path to the sea wall at Foreness Point the youngest beds of chalk are exposed. Very careful and diligent scrutiny of these weathered exposures may yield the rather rare crinoid *Uintacrinus anglicus* (Figure 66). Those who have previously studied the Seaford Head and Black Rock sections at the same levels will be struck by the absence of marl seams but also by the similarity of the well developed, rounded flints similar to the Friar's Bay Flints with which they are correlated. These contrast with the flints below which are peppered with the trace fossil *Chondrites*. Flint *form* is surprisingly consistent in the basin.

The only younger chalk in the North Downs in basal beds of the *Offaster pilula* Zone has been recently recorded in a small pit at Broadstairs by Shephard-Thorn (1988).

Having completed this itinerary, regulars often stop at the Wind Sheaf pub!

Locality 4. Epple Bay, Birchington (TR 307698).

Summary of geological interest

Faulted and strongly jointed Margate Chalk Member; Quaternary thermocast features and dissolution pipes.

This extra stop is for the real specialists interested in the tectonic structure of the Thanet coast chalk and Quaternary cold (and humid) climate structures. Vehicles can be parked along the coast road around to the golf course where there are good views of the low chalk cliffs east to Margate and west to Greenham Bay. Access to the beach is either down the ramp at the centre of Epple Bay or by steps on the east side of the Bay. A sea-wall extends around Epple Bay but there are unprotected cliffs between Epple Bay and Westgate-on-Sea. At low tide on the eastern headland of the bay, a few nodular-flints, preserving strongly developed trace-fossils, can be seen in the chalk wave-cut platform. The chalk cliffs (Margate Chalk Member) are virtually flintless with a single sheet-flint present towards the top of the cliffs on the eastern headland of Epple Bay and continuing east towards Westgate-on-sea. The chalk is regularly and closely jointed with the same dominant trend between 310° and 330° as on the south Thanet coast at Pegwell Bay. A similar frequency and style of faulting is also present.

Epple Bay is formed in the axis of a small dry valley with extensive Quaternary (thermocast?) features. Dissolution pipes are present on the west side of the bay access ramp, above the sea-wall, containing collapse-laminated sediments. On the east side, involutions are buried beneath younger sediments.

ACKNOWLEDGEMENTS

Immense support has been provided by all the landowners in the area both in showing interest and allowing continuous access to quarries. These include Glynde and Firle Estates around Lewes and their agents Strutt & Parker, Rugby Portland Cement at Southerham, Lewes and Halling, Rochester; Blue Circle Industries at Asham and Shoreham Cement Works in Sussex and the Swanscombe - Northfleet and Medway quarries of Kent; and Artex Ltd at Tarring Neville and Meeching Quarries, Newhaven. East Sussex County Engineers Department drilled our research boreholes which were geophysically logged by Southern Water Authority. Numerous other logs and cored boreholes have been provided by the former Southern Water Authority now partly held by the NRA and Southern Science, and the Eastbourne Water Company. The British Geological Survey have generously made all their data available from boreholes and sections in the region. I am particularly grateful to Chris Wood for proof reading the final draft and for many years of joint fieldwork in the region.

FURTHER READING

ALLEN, P. 1975. The Wealden of the Weald: a new model. *Proceedings of the Geologists' Association,* **86,** 389-437.

——1981. Pursuit of Wealden Models. *Journal of the Geological Society, London,* **138,** 375-406.

BAILEY, H. W., GALE, A. S., MORTIMORE, R. N., SWIECICKI, & C. J. WOOD. 1983. The Coniacian-Maastrichtian Stages in the United Kingdom, with particular reference to southern England. *Newsletters on Stratigraphy,* **12,** 19-42.

——1984. Biostratigraphical criteria for recognition of the Coniacian to Maastrichtian stage boundaries in the Chalk of north-west Europe, with particular reference to southern England. *Bulletin of the Geological Society of Denmark,* **33,** 31-39.

BARCHI, P. 1995. *Géochimie et Magnetostratigraphie du Campanien de l'Europe du Nord-Ouest.* These de Doctorat et l'Universite Pierre et Marie Curie (Paris VI), 257pp. plus appendices.

BARCHI, P., GALBRUN, B., MORTIMORE, R.N, POMEROL, B. & M. RENARD. 1996. Litho-, bio- and magnetostratigraphy of the Anglo-Paris Basin Lower Campanian Chalk. 5th. Int. Cret. Symp., Freiberg.

BARROIS, C. 1876. Recherches sur le terrain Crétacée supérieur de Angleterre et de l'Irlande. *Mémoires de la Société Géologique du Nord,* **1,** 234 pp.

BIRKELUND, T., HANCOCK, J. M., HART, M. B., RAWSON, P. F., REMANE, J., ROBASZYNSKI, K, SCHMID, F. & F. SURLYK. 1984. Cretaceous stage boundaries Proposals. *Bulletin of the Geological Society Denmark,* **33,** 3-20.

BRISTOW, C.R., MORTIMORE, R.N. & WOOD, C.J. (In prep). Lithostratigraphy for mapping the Chalk of southern England. *Proceedings of the Geologists' Association.*

BROMLEY, R. G.1967. Some observations on burrows of thalassinidean Crustacea in chalk hardgrounds. *Quarterly Journal of the Geological Society of London,* **123,** 157-182.

——1975. Trace fossils at omission surfaces. In: Frey, R. (ed.), *The study of trace fossils.* Springer-Verlag. 399-428.

——& A. A EKDALE. 1984. *Chondrites:* A trace fossil indicator of anoxia in sediments. *Science,* **224,** 872-874.

—— SCHULZ, M. G. & N. B. PEAKE. 1975. Paramoudras: giant flints, long burrows and early diagenesis of chalks. *Kongelige danske Videnskabernes Selskab Biologiske Skrifter,* **20/10,** 3lpp.

BRYDONE, R. M. 1914. The Zone of *Offaster pilula* in the south English Chalk. Parts I-IV. *Geological Magazine,* **6,** 359-69, 405-11, 449-57, 509-13.

——1915. The *Marsupites* Chalk of Brighton. *Geological Magazine,* **7,** 12-15.

——1939. The Chalk Zone of *Offaster pilula.* London, Dulau & Co., Ltd., 8pp.

CARTER, D. J. & M. B. HART. 1977. Aspects of mid-Cretaceous stratigraphical micropalaeontology. *Bulletin British Museum Natural Histoty (Geology)*, **29**, 1 - 135

CLAYTON, C. J. 1986. The chemical environment of flint formation in Upper Cretaceous chalks. In (Sieveking, G. de G. & M. B. Hart eds.), *The Scientific Study of Flint and Chert.* Cambridge University Press. pp 43-54.

DIBLEY, G. E. 1906. Excursion to Lewes. *Proceedings of the Geologists' Association*, **19**, 1-452.

DITCHFIELD, P. & J.D. MARSHALL, 1989. Isotopic variation in rhythmically bedded chalks: Palaeotemperature variation in the Upper Cretaceous. *Geology*, **17**, 842-845.

DRUMMOND, P. V. 0. 1970. The Mid-Dorset Swell. Evidence of Albian-Cenomanian movements in Wessex. *Proceedings of the Geologists' Association*, **81**, 679-714.

——1983. The *Micraster* biostratigraphy of the Senonian White Chalk of Sussex, southern England. *Geologie Mediterraneenne*, **X**, 177-82.

EKDALE, A. A. 1985. Trace fossils and Mid-Cretaceous anoxic events in the Atlantic Ocean. *Society Economic Paleontologists Mineralogists, 1985*, 333-342.

FELDER, P.J. 1981. Mesofossielen in de kalkafzettingen uit het Krijt van Limburg. *Publ. Natuurhist. Genootschap in Limburg*, **31**, 1-35.

FERRÉ, B., BARCHI, P., MORTIMORE, R.N. & B. POMEROL 1996. Microfaunal assemblages of the Cenomanian-Turonian boundary at Beachy Head (Sussex, UK). Fifth International Cretaceous Symposium, Freiberg, Saxony, Germany. Abstract Volume.

FOOKES, P.G. & BEST, R. 1969. Consolidation characteristics of some late Pleistocene periglacial metastable soils of east Kent. *Quarterly Journal of Engineering Geology*, **2**, 103-128.

GALE, AS. 1989. Field Meeting at Folkestone Warren, 29th November, 1987. *Proceedings of the Geologists' Association*, **100**, 73-80.

GALE, A.S. 1990. A Milankovitch scale for Cenomanian time. *Terra Nova*, **1**, 420-425.

GALE, A.S. 1995. Cyclostratigraphy and correlation of the Cenomanian Stage in Western Europe. In: (House, M.R. & Gale, S. (eds)), *Orbital Forcing Timescales and Cyclostratigraphy.* Geological Society Special Publication. No. **85**, pp.177-197.

GALE A.S., JENKYNS, H.C., KENNEDY, W.J. & R.M. CORFIELD. 1993. Chemostratigraphy versus biostratigraphy: data from around the Cenomanian - Turonian boundary. *Journal of the Geological Society, London*, **150**, 29-32.

GARRISON, R. E. & W. J. KENNEDY. 1977. Origin of solution seams and flaser structure in Upper Cretaceous chalks in southern England. *Sedimentary Geology*, **19**, 107-137.

GASTER, C. T. A. 1924. The Chalk of the Worthing District of Sussex. *Proceedings of the Geologists' Assocation*, **35**, 89-110.

HANCOCK, J.M. 1975a. The Petrology of the Chalk. *Proceedings of the Geologists' Association,* **86,** 499-535.

——1975b. The sequence of facies in the Upper Cretaceous of northern Europe compared with that in the Western Interior. In (Caldwell, W. G. E. ed.), *Special Paper Geologists' Assocation of Canada,* **13,** 83-118.

HARRIS, C.S. & S.T. WARREN. 1996. Chapter 29. UK ground conditions: a geological explanation. In: HARRIS, C.S., HART, M.B., VARLEY, P.M. & C.D. WARREN. 1996. *Engineering Geology of the Channel Tunnel.* Thomas Telford. London. pp. 444-454.

HAYWARD, J. F. 1940. Some variations in *Echinocorys* in southeastern England. *Proceedings Geologists' Assocation,* **51,** 291-310.

HIGGINBOTTOM, I.M. 1966. The Engineering Geology of chalk. In: *Chalk in Earthworks and Foundations.* Proceedings of a Symposium Institution of Civil Engineers, 1966. pp. 1-14.

HUTCHINSON, J.N. 1968. Field Meeting on the Coastal Landslides of Kent. *Proceedings of the Geologists' Assocation,* **79,** 227-237

HUTCHINSON, J.N. 1969. A reconsideration of the coastal landslides at Folkestone Warren, Kent. *Géotechnique,* **19,** 6-38.

HUTCHINSON, J.N. 1970. Field and Laboratory studies of a fall in Upper Chalk cliffs at Joss Bay, Isle of Thanet. *Proceedings of the Roscoe Memorial Synposium.* Cambridge. Also in Hoek E. & Bray J.W. 1981. *Rock Slope* Engineering. Institution of Mining and Metallurgy. pp. 190-196.

JARVIS, I., CARSON, G., COOPER,M.K.E., HART, M.B., LEARY, P.N., TOCHER, B.A., HORNE, D. & ROSENFELD, A. 1988. Microfossil assemblages and the Cenomarian - Turonian (Upper Cretaceous) Oceanic Anoxic Event. *Cretaceous Research,* **9,** 3-103.

JEANS, C.V., LONG, D., HALL, M.A., BLAND, D.I & CORNFORD, C. 1991. The geochemistry of the Plenus Marls at Dover, England: evidence of fluctuating oceanographic conditions and glacial control during the development of the Cenomanian - Turonian $\delta^{13}C$ anomaly. *Geological Magazine,* **128,** 603-632.

JEFFERIES, R. P. S. 1963. The stratigraphy of the *Actinocamax plenus* Subzone (Turonian) in the Anglo-Paris Basin. *Proceedings of the Geologists' Association,* **74,** 1-33.

JENKYNS, H.C., GALE, AS. & R.M. CORFJELD. 1994. Carbon- and oxygen-isotope stratigraphy of the English Chalk and Italian Scaglia and its palaeoclimatic significance. *Geological Magazine,* **131,** 1-34.

JONES, D.K.C. 1981. *Southeast and Southern England.* Methuen. London and New York. 332pp.

JUKES-BROWNE, A. J. & W. HILL. 1903-4. The Cretaceous Rocks of Britain, 2 & 3: the Lower, Middle and Upper Chalk of England. *Memoir of the Geological Survey U. K.*

KENNEDY, W. 1 1967a. Field Meeting at Eastbourne, Sussex. Lower Chalk sedimentation. *Proceedings of the Geologists' Association,* **77,** 365-70.

—— 1967b. Burrows and surface traces from the Lower Chalk of southern England. *Bulletin of the British Museum, Natural History (Geology),* **15,** 125-67.

—— 1969. The correlation of the Lower Chalk of south-east England. *Proceedings of the Geologists' Association,* **80,** 459-551.

—— & R. E. GARRISON. 1975. Morphology and genesis of nodular chalks and hardgrounds in the Upper Cretaceous of southern England. *Sedimentology,* **22,** 311-386.

KERNEY, M.P. 1963. Late glacial deposits on the Chalk of south-east England. *Philosophical Transactions Royal Society, London,* **B246,** 203-254.

KERNEY, M.P., BROWN, E.H. & T.1 CHANDLER. 1964. The late-glacial and post-glacial history of the Chalk escarpment near Brook, Kent. *Philosophical Transactions Royal Society, London,* **B248,** 135-204.

KING, W. B. R. 1954. The geological history of the English Channel *Quarterly Journal of the Geological Society of London,* **110,** 77-101.

LAKE, R. D. 1975. The structure of the Weald - a review. *Proceedings of the Geologists' Association,* **86,** 549-558.

LAKE, R.D., YOUNG, B., WOOD, C.J. & R.N. MORTIMORE. 1987. Geology of the Country around Lewes. *Memoir of the British Geological Survey, G.B.*

LAUTRIDOU, J.P., LETAVERNIER, G., LINDÉ, K, ETLICHER, B. & J.C. OZOUF. 1986. Porosity and frost susceptibility of flints and chalk: laboratory experiments, comparison of 'glacial' and 'periglacial' surface texture of flint materials, and field investigations. In: (G. de G. Sieveking & M.B. Hart eds.), *The Scientific study of flint and chert.* Proceedings of the fourth international symposium held at Brighton Polytechnic, April 1983. Cambridge University Press. pp. 269-282.

MANTELL, G. A 1822. *The Fossils of the South Downs or Illustrations of the Geology of Sussex.* Lepton Relfe, London.

MARSHALL, J.D. 1992. Climatic and oceanographic isotopic signals from the carbonate rock record and their preservation. *Geological Magazine,* **129,** 143-160.

MORTIMORE, R. N. 1979. *The relationship of stratigraphy and tectonofacies to the physical properties of the White Chalk of Sussex.* CNAA Ph.D. Thesis, Brighton Polytechnic. 5 vols.

MORTIMORE, R. N. 1983. The stratigraphy and sedimentation of the Turonian-Campanian in the Southern Province of England. *Zitteliana,* **10,** 27-41.

—— 1986a. Stratigraphy of the Upper Cretaceous White Chalk of Sussex. *Proceedings of the Geologists' Association,* **97,** 97-139.

—— 1986b. Controls on Upper Cretaceous sedimentation in the South Downs with particular reference to flint distribution. In (G. de G. Sieveking, & M. B. Hart eds.), *The scientific study of flint and chert.* Cambridge University Press, pp 21-42.

——1987. Upper Cretaceous Chalk in the North and South Downs, England: a correlation. *Proceedings of the Geologists' Association,* **98,** 77-86

—— & C. J. WOOD. 1986. The distribution of flint in the English Chalk, with particular reference to the 'Brandon Flint Series' and the high Turonian flint maximum. In (G. de G Sieveking & M. B. Hart eds.), *The scientlfic study of flint and chert,* Cambridge University Press, pp 7-20.

—— & B. POMEROL. 1987. Correlation of the Upper Cretaceous White Chalk (Turonian to Campanian) in the Anglo-Paris Basin. *Proceedings of the Geologists' Association,* **98,** 97-143.

MORTIMORE, R.N. & POMEROL, B. 1991a. Upper Cretaceous tectonic disruptions in a placid Chalk sequence in the Anglo-Paris Basin. *Journal of the Geological Society, London,* **148,** 391-404.

MORTIMORE, R.N. & POMEROL, B. 1991b. Stratigraphy and Eustatic Implications of Trace Fossil Events in the Upper Cretaceous Chalk of Northern Europe. *Palaios,* **6,** 216-231.

MORTIMORE R.N. & B. POMEROL. 1996. A revision of Turonian litho- and biostratigraphy in the Anglo-Paris Basin. *Mitteilungen aus dem Geologisch-Paläontologischen Institut der Universitat Hamburg.* **77,** 423-441.

MORTIMORE, R.N., POMEROL, B. & J. LAMONT-BLACK 1996. Chapter 28. Examples of structural and sedimentological controls on chalk engineering behaviour. In: Harris, C.S., Hart, M.B., Varley, P.M. & C.D. Warren (eds.). 1996. *Engineering Geology of the Channel Tunnel.* Thomas Telford. London. pp. 436-443.

OWEN, E. & A.B. SMITH. 1987. *Fossils of the Chalk.* Palaeontological Association Field Guides: No. 2. Palaeontological Association, London.

PAUL, C.R.C., MITCHELL, S.F., MARSHALL, J.D., LEARY, P.N., GALE, AS., DUANE, AM., & DITCHFIELD, P.W. 1994. Palaeoceanographic events in the Middle Cenomanian of Northwest Europe. *Cretaceous Research,* **15,** 707-738.

PENNING, W. H. & A. J. JUKES-BROWNE. 1881. The Geology of the neighbourhood of Cambridge. *Memoir of the Geological Survey G.B.*

PITCHER, W.S., SHEARMAN, D.J. & PUGH, D.C. 1954. The loess of Pegwell Bay, Kent and its associated frost soils. *Geological Magazine,* **91,** 308-314.

PITCHER, W.S., PEAKE, N.B., CARRECK, J.N., KIRKALDY, J.F. & HANCOCK, J.M. 1967. The *London Region (South of the Thames).* Geologists' Association Guide No.30B. Revised edition 1967, Benham & Company Ltd., Colchester. 32pp.

POMEROL. B. 1976. La connaissance des paléo-océans: données fournies par l'étude des formations sédimentaires des marges continentales. *C.R. Acad. Sci. Paris,* **284,** 341-344.

POMEROL, B. 1976. Géochimie des craies du cap d'Antifer (Haute-Normandie). *Bull. Soc. géol. France,* XVIII, 1051-1060.

POMEROL, B. 1983. Geochemistry of the Late Cenomanian - Early Turonian Chalks of the Anglo-Paris Basin: Manganese and Carbon Isotopes in Carbonates as Palaeoceanographic indicators. *Cretaceous Research,* **4,** 85-93.

POMEROL, B., BAILEY, H.W., MONCIARDINI, C. & R.N. MORTIMORE. 1987. Lithostratigraphy and Biostratigraphy of the Lewes and Seaford Chalks: a link across the Anglo-Paris Basin at the Turonian-Senonian boundary. *Cretaceous Research,* **8,** 289-304.

POMEROL, B. & MORTIMORE, R.N. 1993. Lithostratigraphy and correlation of the Cenomanian - Turonian boundary sequence. *Newsletters on Stratigraphy,* **28,** 59-78.

PRATT, L.M. FORCE, E.R. & B. POMEROL 1991. Coupled manganese and carbon-isotopic events in marine carbonates at the Cenomanian - Turonian boundary. *Journal of Sedimentary Petrology,* **61,** 370-383.

ROBINSON, N.D. 1986. Lithostratigraphy of the Chalk Group of the North Downs, southeast England. *Proceedings of the Geologists' Association,* **97,** 141-70.

ROWE, A. W. 1899. An analysis of the genus *Micraster,* as determined by rigorous zonal collecting from the Zone of *Rhynchonella cuvieri* to that of *Micraster coranguinum. Quarterly Journal of the Geological Society, of London,* **55,** 494.

—— 1900. The Zones of the White Chalk of the English coast I. Kent and Sussex. *Proceedings of the Geologist's Association,* **16,** 289-368.

—— 1908. The Zones of the White Chalk of the English coast V. The Isle of Wight. *Proceedings of the Geologist's Association,* **20,** 209-352.

RUFFELL, A., ROSS, A. & TAYLOR, K. 1996. *Early Cretaceous Environments of the Weald.* Geologists' Association Guide No. 55 81 pp.

SHEPHARD-THORN, E.R. 1988. Geology of the country around Ramsgate and Dover. *Memoir of the British Geological Survey. G.B.*

STILLE, 1924. *Grundfragen der vergleichenden Tektonik.* Berlin (Borntraeger). 443pp. 14 figs.

STOKES, R. B. 1977. The echinoids *Micraster* and *Epiaster* from the Turonian and Senonian chalk of England. *Palaeontology,* **20,** 805-21.

STRAHAN, A. 1896. On a phosphatic chalk with *Holaster planus* at Lewes. *Quarterly Journal of the Geological Society, of London,* **52,** 463.

TOMS, A.H. 1946. Folkestone Warren Landslips: Research carried out in 1939 by the Southern Railway Company. *Proceedings of the Institution of Civil Engineers.* Railway Paper No.19, 3-44.

ULICNÝ D., HLADÍKOVÁ, I & L. HRADECKÁ.1993. Record of sea-level changes, oxygen depletion and the $\delta^{13}C$ anomaly across the Cenomanian - Turonian boundary, Bohemian Cretaceous Basin. *Cretaceous Research,* **14,** 211-234.

ULICNÝ D., HLADÍKOVÁ, J. ATTREP, M.J. Jr., CECH, S., HRADECKÁ, L & M. SVOBODOVÁ. 1996. Sea-level changes and geochemical anomalies across the Cenomanian - Turonian boundary, Pecínov Quarry, Bohemia. *Palaeogeography, Palaeoclimatology, Palaeocology.* (In Press).

VOIGT, E. 1929. Die lithogenese der Flach- und Tiefwassersedimente des jüngeren Oberkreide-meeres. *Jb. Halleschen Verb. Eforsch. mitteldeutsch. Bodensch.,* N.F., **8,** 2, 3-162, 13 plates, Halle/S.

VOIGT, E. 1963. Über Randtröge vor Schollenrändern und ihre Bedeutung im

Gebiet der mitteleuropäischen Senke und angrenzender Gebiete. z. dt. geol ges., 114, 378-418. Hannover.

VOIGT, T., VOIGT, S. & K.-A. TRÖGER. 1994. Fazies-Entwicklung einer ertrunkenen Felsküste-die obercenomane Monzonitklippe westlich von Dresden. (Facies development of a drowned rocky coast - the Upper Cenomanian Monzonite-Cliff near Dresden). *Freiberger Forschungsheft,* **C452,** 23-34. Leipzig, 1994. (all fig. captions in this paper in both German and English and an English abstract).

WHITE, H. J. O. 1924. The Geology of the country near Brighton and Worthing. *Memoir Geological Survey G.B.*

WHITE, H.J.O. 1926. The Geology of the country near Lewes. *Memoir of the Geological Survey G.B.*

WILMOT, R.D. & YOUNG, B. 1985. Aluminite and other aluminium minerals from Newhaven, Sussex: the first occurrence of Nordstrandite in Great Britain. *Proceedings of the Geologists' Association,* **96,** 47-52.

WOOD, C.J. Field Meeting on the Lower Chalk between Folkestone and Dover. *Proceedings of the Geologists' Association,* **76,** 301-304.

WOOD C.J. & MORTIMORE, R.N. 1995. An anomalous Black Band succession (Cenomanian - Turonian boundary interval) at Melton Ross, Lincolnshire, eastern England and its international significance. *Berliner geowissenschaftliche Abhandlungen,* E16 Gudolf-ERNST-Festschrift, 277-287 Berlin.

WOOLDRIDGE, S.W. & F. GOLDRING. 1953. *The Weald.* Collins, London. 276pp.

WRAY, D. 1990. *The petrology of clay-rich beds in the Turonian (Upper Cretaceous) of the Anglo-Paris Basin.* PhD. Thesis, CNAA/City of London Polytechnic, London.

WRAY, D. 1995. Origin of clay-rich beds in Turonian chalks from Lower Saxony, Germany - a rare-earth element study. *Chemical Geology.* **119,** 161-173.

WRAY, D. S. & A.S. GALE. 1993. Geochemical correlation of marl bands in Turonian chalks of the Anglo-Paris Basin. (In: Hailwood E.A. & Kidd, R.B. eds.), *High Resolution Stratigraphy.* Geological Society Special Publication No.70, pp. 211-226.

WRIGHT, C.W. & E.V. WRIGHT. 1951. A survey of the fossil cephalopoda of Great Britain. *Palaeontographical Society* [*Monograph.*], 40pp.

YOUNG, B. 1978. *The Upper Greensand of Eastbourne, Sussex.* In: Guide Book to South East England Excursion, Sixth International Clay Conference, Oxford, 48-52.

YOUNG, B. & R. A. MONKHOUSE. 1980. The Geology and Hydrogeology of the Lower Greensand of the Sompting Borehole, West Sussex. *Proceedings of the Geologists' Association,* **91,** 307-313.

YOUNG, B. & R.D. LAKE. 1988. Geology of the country around Brighton and Worthing. *Memoir of the British Geological Survey, G.B.*

GEOLOGISTS' ASSOCIATION GUIDES

The following are available from **Geological Society Publishing House, Unit 7, Brassmill Enterprise Centre, Brassmill Lane, Bath, BA1 3JN.** Credit card orders are accepted by telephone or fax. Tel: 01225 445046. Fax: 01225 442836.

No 2 The Lake District 1990
No 7 Geology of Manchester Area 1991
No 19 West Cornwall 1994
No 23 Dorset 1993
No 32 Isle of Arran 1989
No 34 Yorkshire Coast 1992
No 42 Mallorca 1990
No 43 Costa Blanca 1990
No 44 Late Precambrian Geology Scottish Highlands and Islands 1991
No 46 Isle of Man 1993
No 47 Coastal Landforms of West Dorset 1992
No 50 Southern Cyprus 1994
No 51 The Island of Bute 1995
No 52 Iceland 1994
No 53 Eastern & Central Jamaica 1995
No 54 Aberystwyth District 1995
No 55 Early Cretaceous Environments of the Weald
No 56 The Castleton Area - Derbyshire - 1996